Juices & Smoothies

An Easy Way to Five-a-Day

Juices & Smoothies

*An Easy Way to
Five-a-Day*

LEE FABER

Abbeydale Press

ISBN 978-1-86147-270-0

1 3 5 7 9 10 8 6 4 2

Published by Abbeydale Press
an imprint of Bookmart Ltd
Registered number 2372865
Trading as Bookmart Ltd
Blaby Road, Wigston, Leicester
LE18 4SE, England

Produced by Omnipress Limited, UK
Cover design by Omnipress Limited, UK

Printed in Dubai

ABOUT THE AUTHOR

Lee Faber is a native-born American who became a
British citizen, having been in the UK since 1981. She
has lived and worked in New York, Florida, London
and now resides in Wiltshire. During her career she
has been involved in book editing and writing with an
emphasis on health, food and cookery. She has
specialised in Americanising/Anglicising books on
a variety of subjects for both US and UK publishers.
She is also the author of *Healthy Oils*, *Aloe Vera* and
Berries in this series. Lee is an accomplished
cook and has created many recipes.

DISCLAIMER

These ideas are passed on in good faith but the
author does not guarantee results, nor cannot be held
responsible for any adverse results.

CONTENTS

INTRODUCTION

The fruit,
the whole fruit
and nothing but the fruit (or veg)

No one would argue that the best way, nutritionally, to have your five fruits and vegetables a day would be to grow them yourself, organically, and eat them in their natural state, raw. But this is neither practical nor, in some cases, desirable.

I used to grow tomatoes, aubergines and peppers in a previous life in New Jersey and the tomatoes hardly ever made their way into my kitchen because they were so delicious picked warm off the vine and popped into our mouths. But I remember my mother telling me about her childhood in Russia where they grew potatoes in their garden and often ate them raw — somehow that doesn't sound very appealing at all to me!

There are obviously some vegetables one doesn't usually eat raw. So the next best thing is to cook them, either with or without their skins. Or is it? And there are some people (one of my grandsons comes to mind) who won't even drink orange juice if it has 'bits' in it.

How do we manage to get the best vitamin punch out of our five a day if we don't have a garden, don't like eating certain things raw, don't like eating certain fruits and vegetables at all or don't like 'bits'?

The answer is JUICE.

There is an almost endless variety of juice to be had, from single fruits and vegetables to mixtures of different varieties; simply squeezed with a very bog-standard, old-fashioned citrus juicer for oranges and lemons to powerful state-of-the-art machines (see Juicing and Smoothie equipment, pages 14–16).

The healthiest juice, in my opinion at least, is the juice squeezed in home kitchens from fresh fruits and vegetables. Making your own juice is a virtuous occupation which most of us don't have the time for, except on leisurely weekends when we don't have to commute to work, do the school run, or be on time for classes. You can make your juice in advance the evening before and refrigerate it, but that option is only marginally better than buying ready-made, because according to the experts, the nutrients are lost very quickly after 12 hours or so.

So, on to ready-made juices for the moment.

EAT WELL AND BE HEALTHY

If you subscribe to a balanced diet, vitamin supplements are not normally necessary. Eat whole food and feel good knowing that you've got nutrition from nature's bounty flowing through your body every day.

HISTORY OF JUICE

When most of us think of juice, the first fruit that comes to mind is orange. I can't remember a time when we didn't have orange juice throughout the year in New York, but I don't remember whether my mother squeezed it – we did have a juice press, so perhaps she did. My American friends remember frozen concentrated orange juice (that was reconstituted with water), but my older British friends don't remember orange juice in any form except powder at home and some sort of orange juice in little bottles from time to time at school. Even in America apparently, prior to 1947, the only way to drink orange juice was to squeeze the ripe fruit into a container through a sieve to remove the seeds and drink it.

Oranges were only available during the peak season for ripe oranges because citrus fruit doesn't ripen further after it's been picked. And if you lived too far away from an orange grove, orange juice wasn't an option at all – you had to make do with apple juice or berry juice.

Further back in history, oranges were not the only fruit or juice.

For hundreds of years, navies around the world issued sailors with a daily tot of rum.

Lauchlin Rose, a descendant of a prominent family of Scottish shipbuilders, founded L. Rose & Company in Edinburgh in 1865. Describing himself as a 'lime and lemon juice merchant', he combined a keen business sense with his knowledge of the sea. Scurvy, caused by a deficiency of vitamin C, had been the scourge of sailors since the early days of sailing ships. To prevent 'this most terrible of the diseases of maritime life', a supply of lime or lemon juice preserved with 15% of rum was generally put on board for long voyages.

In 1867, Lauchlin developed and patented a process that effectively prevented fermentation and preserved fruit juice without alcohol. The same year, the Merchant Shipping Act was passed, whereby all vessels, Royal Navy and Merchant, were required to carry lime juice for a daily ration to ships' companies. It was this enactment that resulted in British sailors being called 'limeys'.

On the other side of the Atlantic, also in the 1860s, another juice was born. Dr Thomas Bramwell Welch, a physician and dentist by profession, successfully pasteurised Concord grape juice (named after Concord, Massachusetts where it originated) to produce an 'unfermented sacramental wine' for fellow parishioners at his church in Vineland, New Jersey, where he was communion steward. His achievement marked the beginning of the American processed fruit juice industry.

JUICING AND SMOOTHIE EQUIPMENT

SIMPLE REAMERS AND SQUEEZERS

The simplest and cheapest extractor for citrus fruit is probably the sort your grandmother had (I still have one). It consists of a bowl and a moulded top. You cut the fruit in half, place it on top of the fruit-shaped squeezer and with your wrist, turn the fruit in semicircles to extract the juice and pulp of lemons, limes, oranges and grapefruit which collects in the bowl and can be poured into a glass or container. They are made of glass, metal or plastic and are easily washed.

CENTRIFUGAL JUICERS

Centrifugal juicers are the most popular and the most affordable type of modern juicers. In fact, most juicers available in department stores and on the high street are centrifugal juice machines.

Centrifugal juicers are great at juicing almost any fruit or vegetable, but are not capable of efficiently extracting juice from wheatgrass, leafy greens or herbs. This type of juicer works by using a flat cutting blade on the bottom of a rapidly spinning basket. First it grates the fruit or vegetable into a pulp, and then it uses centrifugal force to push the pulp against a strainer screen by spinning it at a very high speed.

MASTICATING JUICERS

Masticating juicers literally chew up fruit and vegetables and press out the juice through a screen. They are available principally online and while they are more expensive than other kinds of juicers, they give the optimum juice yield and retain more nutrients. They are also capable of extracting juice from grasses, leafy greens and herbs. Health enthusiasts who want better performance than what they are getting from their existing machines usually choose masticating juicers.

Another benefit of masticating juicers is that they operate at slower speeds (r.p.m.) than centrifugal juicers, resulting in less foam and heat, which means more nutrition in your glass.

Twin-gear (triturating) juicers are the most expensive type of juicers, but they offer the most benefits. These juicers turn at even slower speeds (r.p.m.), resulting in even less oxidation from foam and less destruction of nutrients from heat. Triturating juicers are the most efficient type of juicer available and can extract larger volumes of juice from fruits, vegetables, wheatgrass, pine needles, spinach, and other greens and herbs.

Twin-gear juicers operate by pressing food between two interlocking roller gears. This juicing process yields a larger volume of juice and extracts more fibre, enzymes, vitamins and trace minerals.

Masticating juicers are also more versatile than centrifugal juicers because, in addition to extracting juices, they also homogenise foods to make baby foods, patés, sauces, nut butters, banana ice creams and fruit sorbets. Some of these juicers can even extrude pasta and make rice cakes!

Wheatgrass juicers are made exclusively for extracting the juice from wheatgrass and other leafy greens, as well as some soft fruits like grapes, but are not for extracting juice from vegetables and most fruits. Wheatgrass juicers are available in both electric and manual models.

Most masticating juicers are capable of extracting juice from wheatgrass, so a specialist juicer is an unnecessary piece of kitchen equipment for all but the highly dedicated wheatgrass juice lovers.

COMMERCIALLY PREPARED JUICE

Orange juice is so popular in the United Kingdom that about 75% of all juice sold here is orange. According to an article published in 2007 in *The Observer*, in a survey of 8- to 11-year-olds, one-third thought oranges grew in the United Kingdom.

Spain is the largest source of United Kingdom citrus fruits, but almost 60% is now imported from outside the EU, with most of the oranges and juice coming from the Americas.

You could be forgiven for thinking that fresh ready-made juice (not from concentrate) is the next best thing to juice just squeezed in your kitchen. I certainly thought that until I started researching this book and discovered there was some disagreement on this point.

TYPES OF READY-SQUEEZED JUICE

Freshly squeezed
Bottles and cartons of freshly squeezed (not-from-concentrate) juice are found in the chiller cabinets of supermarkets, little corner shops, petrol stations, sandwich bars, delis . . . everywhere, in fact, ranging from single portions to family size. The advantage of freshly squeezed juice is that, ideally, it is only juice, with nothing added, and is the closest in taste to squeezing it yourself. The downside is that if you are not buying a single-portion size, it must always be refrigerated, has a use-by date and should be consumed within five days after opening. It also needs to be well shaken before every use, otherwise you end up with very thin juice at the beginning of the carton or bottle and very thick juice as you get to the

bottom. And it may not be 'only juice'. Although it is pressed directly from the fruit, not from concentrate, it might be pasteurised during packing, citric acid or ascorbic acid might have been added and, in some cases, salt. Some juices also include other nutrients such as calcium and vitamin D.

Pure from concentrate

One of the first benefits of concentrated juice is that it allowed those in colder climates to enjoy orange juice all year round and made other, more exotic juices available. Plus the 'season' for all types of juice was extended indefinitely. Concentrated juice goes through a vacuum evaporation process, in which it loses some of its oily flavouring essences (which are added back after concentrating the juice). Some juice concentrate is simply reconstituted at a packaging plant and put into cartons like not-from-concentrate juice. Once packaged, reconstituted juice is kept refrigerated and carries the same shelf-life as freshly squeezed juice.

Frozen concentrate

I haven't seen any frozen concentrated juice in the UK for 10 years or so, but it is still very popular in the USA. Preservatives can be added to frozen concentrated juice, but they are often left out because it is shipped frozen and safely kept that way. If you see it at all in shops, you will find it in the freezer section.

Manufacturers of pasteurised, not-from-concentrate juice would lead you to believe that their product is fresher and better for you than juice from concentrate. But this may not be the case. Juice that is not concentrated is too oily, so it has to be 'de-oiled' before pasteurising or freezing. If the juice isn't frozen, its shelf-life is less than three weeks. And from what I read, in order to ensure that juice is available all year round, a significant portion of this 'fresh' juice must be frozen for long periods of time. Preservatives may be added to defer spoilage.

If you are not squeezing your juice yourself, which type of commercial juice is better for you then? Freshly squeezed? Pure concentrate? Frozen concentrate?

Some scientists believe that frozen concentrated orange juice is actually better for you in terms of vitamin content and sugar. Vitamin C, the 'sunshine vitamin', is higher in concentrated juice since it degrades significantly over time whenever the temperature of the product is above freezing. The nutritional tables also indicate that not-from-concentrate orange juice contains a higher level of simple sugars.

To further confuse the issue there are the juice drinks.

Fruit juices contain 100% juice from a single juice or a juice blend and typically have no sugar or sweeteners added. Fruit juice drinks, juice cocktails, fruit ades and squashes contain less than 100% juice; many contain only 5% or 10% fruit juice. Most nutritionists believe that 100% fruit juice with natural sugars that have come from the fruit itself is better than a fruit drink with added sugar.

FRUIT
JUICES

AÇAI

Açai is a little purple Brazilian rainforest berry with two very important attributes: it has the highest antioxidant value of any fruit and is one of the lowest in sugar. It claims to have 60% more antioxidants than pomegranate, with almost no naturally occurring sugar.

Since this is not one of the berries that Britons can pick or buy in the supermarket (at least not yet), the best product to purchase is frozen pulp, especially if you want to make your own juices or smoothies. The frozen pulp retains all the nutritional properties, which are released when you blend it with your favourite juice, fruit or yoghurt.

Another excellent way of buying Açai is as a freeze-dried powder. The freeze-drying process retains all the nutritional properties of Açai through reducing the pulp to a fine powder at very low temperatures. Unlike extracts, freeze-dried Açai completely captures the unique synergy of the nutritional benefits found in Açai and is completely pure with no carrying agents. It is simply pure Açai and is an excellent addition to any beverage!

Both products can be purchased on the Internet — the frozen pulp in quantities as small as 3 kg/6.6 lb (30 x 100 g/3$\frac{1}{2}$ oz sachets) and the freeze-dried product in 90 g/3 oz tubs.

Once thawed and bottled, Açai loses many of its natural characteristics and nutritional properties. The bottled form is also a less consistent way of using Açai, since some ready-made juices will often contain very little Açai pulp. This is the major reason why the vast majority of Açai in Brazil is consumed in the form of frozen fruit pulp. The best bottled juices are 100% Açai, sweetened with agave rather than sugar. Other high-quality Açai juices are mixed with mango, blueberry, passion fruit or raspberry.

Açai juice may be purchased in most wholefood and health food shops. Açai juice blends and juice drinks can also be bought at some supermarkets.

APPLE

The wild apple of ancient Asia would never have made it to the modern table in its uncultivated form. The trees produced hundreds of tiny sour fruits consisting mostly of numerous, small, dark brown seeds and core, hardly a fruit that anyone would anticipate eating. The wild apple of Europe is thought to be the main ancestor of the domestic apple.

Though some historians are in dispute over exactly who first cultivated the wild apple, many believe it was the Romans who discovered they could cultivate these gnarly wild apples into fleshy, sweet and juicy fruits. Some historians report the apple's origins were rooted in South Western Asia. Others note that apple seeds found in Anatolia were carbon dated to 6500 BC. Archaeologists even found a fossilised imprint of an apple seed from the Neolithic period in England.

With the apple's exact origin in question, another dilemma arises. Did Eve really bite into an apple that she plucked off the forbidden tree of knowledge of good and evil in the Garden of Eden? No specific name is given to the fruit she tasted from that tree, though apples are mentioned later in the Bible. Some historians believe Eve's fruit of temptation might have been a pomegranate or possibly even a quince.

Many foods have been thought to possess magical qualities and even aphrodisiac powers. The apple's projected powers could fill a bushel of folklore.

An Ancient Greek who wanted to propose to a woman would only have to toss her an apple. If she caught it, he knew she had accepted his offer.

In Germany, during medieval times, a man who ate an apple that was steeped in the perspiration of the woman he loved was very likely to succeed in the relationship.

Here's a simple, cost-effective and long-forgotten fertility rite to share with those desirous of conceiving a healthy apple harvest. Villagers would select the largest apple tree in the orchard, and hang cider-soaked pieces of toast on its branches to attract robins. To those villagers, robins were considered the good spirits of the tree. Then, to drive away the evil spirits, the people would gather throughout the orchard and fire many blasts from their shotguns. They followed this ritual by pouring cider over the tree's roots and tippled a few cups themselves. Merriment followed with dancing around the tree with their arms linked as they chanted ancient charms. Even today some highly superstitious people believe this practice is necessary to ensure a good crop of apples.

Some unique and curious customs have faded into obscurity. Long ago, in Cumberland (now Cumbria), England, people would suspend apples from strings over the hearth. When the apples were fully roasted, they fell into a bowl of spiced, mulled wine that was waiting for them beneath. This practice was actually the precursor to the oven-baked apple of today.

Throughout history apples have symbolised luxury, pleasure, love, fertility and even jealousy. Greek mythology recounts this tale: from the garden of the Hesperides, golden apples were given to Hera as a wedding gift at her marriage to Zeus. Modern Greek scholars believe that the golden apples of the Hesperides were actually oranges or lemons.

It is told that the prophet Muhammad inhaled the fragrance of an apple brought to him by an angel just before his last breath of life.

Apple trees are never very far away in Britain as our climate is conducive to producing an abundance of succulent apples. (And probably the most varieties of apple as well — certainly many hundreds, some say more than 2,000, although you would be pushed to find more than a few in our supermarkets.) Supermarkets are not the best places to look. Better bets are farm shops, farmers' markets and fruit growers or perhaps even a local greengrocer if you can still find one. (They are also the best sources for apple juice.)

Apples are one of the most popular fruits in the world. Eating apples offers more health benefits than drinking apple juice as you also get the fibre in apples. And unless you have an apple press or a juicer, you will have to content yourself with store-bought apple juice, which can be very good indeed.

When buying apple juice, cloudy is a healthier option than clear, according to Polish scientists. The manufacturing process used to make clear apple juice, which includes using an enzyme to break down the pectin in apple cell walls and spinning to remove pulp, considerably decreases the levels of polyphenols in the end product.

A senior research scientist at the Institute of Food Research in Norwich said that clear apple juices tended to be more popular and are more stable, giving them a longer shelf-life. He stated:

A lot of polyphenols are lost when you make a clear juice. It could also be that because you're retaining that cloudiness and pectin there's the additional benefit of fibre.

Remember the old adage 'An apple a day keeps the doctor away'? As with many old wives' tales, there is probably more than an apple seed of truth in it.

APRICOT

One of the last fruits of summer, the apricot is beautiful, orange-coloured and full of betacarotene and fibre. Although dried and tinned apricots are available year-round, fresh apricots with a plentiful supply of vitamin C enjoy a very short season in Britain — usually late summer. Any fresh fruit you see during the winter months has been imported from warmer climes.

Relatives of peaches, apricots have velvety skin and flesh and are not too juicy, but definitely smooth and sweet. Some describe their flavour as almost musky, with a faint tartness that lies somewhere between a peach and a plum.

Originally, apricots came from China but arrived in Europe via Armenia, which is why the scientific name is *Prunus armenaica*. Apricots are enjoyed as a fresh fruit, but are also very popular dried, cooked into pastry, and eaten as jam. The fruits are also distilled into brandy and liqueur. Essential oil from the stones is sold commercially as bitter almond oil. Turkey, Italy, Russia, Spain, Greece, the USA and France are the leading producers of apricots.

If you are lucky enough to have an apricot tree in your garden or access to a farm that grows apricots, look for fruits with a rich orange colour, avoiding those that are pale and yellow. Fruits should be slightly soft. If they are too firm they have not been tree-ripened, and tree-ripened fruits always taste best.

For the best antioxidant content, choose fully ripened fruit. If you find apricots that are plump, firm and orange-gold in colour, they'll be ready to eat after about two days of ripening at room temperature. Don't buy hard fruits that are tinged with green — they will never develop full flavour.

Even when not fully ripe, apricots should yield to gentle pressure and exude a perfumed fragrance; their skin should be smooth and velvety. Avoid any that have shrivelled skin or bruises; however, minor blemishes that do not break the skin will not affect the flavour.

Research conducted at the University of Innsbruck in Austria suggests that as fruits fully ripen, almost to the point of spoilage, their antioxidant levels actually increase.

There is some controversy about whether apricot kernels should be eaten because of their cyanide content, but you should be cautious about chewing on the stems: release of hydrogen cyanide gas, from the plant compounds called prussic acid, is what mystery writers refer to as the smell of bitter almonds on the breath.

Apricot juice is very nutritious. Apricot has about as much vitamin C in its fruit whether it is gathered ripe or quite hard. On the other hand, the carotene builds up to a high level during the final ripening period so that the fully tree-ripened apricot has more than 200% extra. Perfectly ripe fruit will keep for only a day or so before becoming unfit to eat. It is therefore best to freeze the juice, if you can. The main use of apricot juice is as an extra provider of vitamin A and as a variation to the flavour when combining with other fruit and vegetable juices.

BLACKBERRY

Blackberries provide nectar for British butterflies in the UK. They also provide delight for humans. The blackberry is one of the most common berries to be found in the wild. It is still prevalent due to its ability to colonise a wide range of habitats. Blackberry juice is sweet and rich-tasting and has a number of health benefiting properties.

Everyone loves blackberry picking — there is something very satisfying about searching through the tangle of thorns for the fattest, glossiest fruit. It's often the first wild food children come across, found both in country and town. We have plenty of blackberries growing wild near where I live and in the summer I sometimes stuff a plastic bag in my pocket to pick them during my morning walk. Some of them inevitably end up in my mouth, unwashed, but nothing bad has ever come from that.

According to legend, Michaelmas (29 September) is the day the Devil spits on blackberries, making them inedible. There is a lot of tannin in blackberries and perhaps at the end of their season when they begin to wither, they are too bitter.

What can you make with the fruit you have picked, apart from the usual jam and apple and blackberry crumble?

When added to smoothies, blackberries are a good source of fibre as they contain the soluble fibre pectin as well as many small seeds (the blackberry is actually made up of a number of individual tiny fruits known as drupelets that each contain a seed).

When juicing them you should look for blackberries that are firm and shiny. Ripe fruit will have a strong aroma. After harvesting, blackberries will perish very quickly (within a few days) so it is essential to try and find the freshest you can (even better to pick your own). If you buy blackberries from a shop, make sure to sort the blackberries when you get home, eating any that are starting to show signs of perishing and removing any with mould or that are badly squashed. Blackberries freeze very well and will keep for around six months so you can enjoy them in your juices and smoothies for most of the year.

The pulp that remains after the juice has been separated can be mixed with filtered water to make naturally flavoured ice lollies. Blackberry ice cubes will also enhance many juice drinks. The virtuous act of retaining the pulp will ensure that the fibre of the blackberries is utilised and these flavoured ice cubes certainly taste good. In fact, you can make ice cubes out of any fruit pulp or juice and add them to a variety of drinks.

Historically, blackberries have been used to treat a number of health conditions including gout, diarrhoea and sore throats. Blackberries are also well known for containing antioxidants that combat harmful free radicals that damage healthy cells and lead to disease. These antioxidants include vitamin C, vitamin E and anthocyanins. Many face creams now contain blackberries and promote 'antioxidant properties' that help prevent signs of ageing in the skin.

BLACKCURRANT

Blackcurrants have grown in the British Isles for over 500 years and have been used by herbalists since the Middle Ages to treat bladder stones and liver disorders, and blended into syrups for coughs and lung ailments. According to The Blackcurrant Foundation, the total British blackcurrant crop can range from 12,000 to 14,000 tonnes a year.

Weight for weight, blackcurrants contain nearly four times as much Vitamin C as an orange.

It may be small, but the mighty blackcurrant is bursting with more health-promoting antioxidants than most other fruit and vegetables, including blueberries!

It's the special antioxidants called anthocyanins which that blackcurrants their distinctive dark colour. British blackcurrants are cultivated especially for their deep colour, which makes them extra good for you.

At one point blackcurrant was a 'forbidden fruit' in America, banned from being farmed for almost 100 years in 1911 because it was thought to carry white pine blister rust, a lethal disease that threatened New York's burgeoning timber industry. Here it has been dubbed the 'forgotten fruit' and a 'superfood' but with new research suggesting that British blackcurrants could be the secret weapons in the fight against Alzheimer's disease, they could now be known as the 'forget-me-not' fruit.

Blackcurrants fight infection as well. The Scottish Crop Research Institute says: 'It is clear from the increasing numbers of scientific studies that the natural compounds found routinely in blackcurrants show a diverse range of antimicrobial activities which may help reduce the incidence of or help alleviate the symptoms of infection by the life threatening ones known as MRSA.' Cranberries are well known for treating urinary tract infections, but blackcurrants play their part as well.

Everyone in Britain knows Ribena — probably because this company's drinks were their first introduction to blackcurrants. Their website states: 'Britain's blackcurrants have one thing in common — they all want to be Ribena blackcurrants when they grow up. They know that ending up in a cool glass of Ribena is the ultimate ambition. Because 95% of all Britain's blackcurrants make it into Ribena.'

As for the other 5%, eating blackcurrants or drinking blackcurrant juice as part of a healthy diet, is an easy, natural way to improve your antioxidant intake and maintain a healthy lifestyle, ward off infections, and a fine way to load the body with their wonderful and delicious components.

BLUEBERRY

For the most part, blue isn't a natural colour for food. How many natural foods can you think of that are blue aside from blueberries and, stretching it a bit, blue cheese?

There is growing evidence that blueberries are an important part of a healthy diet. Using a test called ORAC (Oxygen Radical Absorbance Capacity), researchers have shown that a serving of fresh blueberries provides more antioxidant activity than many other fresh fruits and vegetables. Blueberries are ranked number one compared with 40 other commercially available fruits and vegetables. Americans have always been partial to blueberries.

Blueberry pie is a classic example. Until recently blueberries weren't particularly popular in the UK. Most people associated them with American muffins, and when they were sold at greengrocers and supermarkets (rarely), they were so expensive as not to be worth buying.

But in the last 5–10 years there has been a sea change due to the blueberry's prominence as a 'superfood'. You can now buy blueberry plants for your garden, pick your own at several farms throughout the country from July–September, and buy blueberries at farm shops, farmers' markets, supermarkets and even local greengrocers.

And in addition to throwing a handful into your morning cereal or fruit and yoghurt, you can buy or make wonderful blueberry juice. In the supermarket you will usually find blueberry juice mixed with pomegranate, cranberry or other fruit because some people find the flavour of blueberry alone too strong. But you should experiment if you are making your own blueberry–apple might be a good place to start.

Blueberries freeze beautifully, so if you have a glut in your garden or find a special at the supermarket, buy them and freeze to use later.

CRANBERRY

The cranberry has distinction in America as a 'wonderberry', with a plethora of good health properties. The berry grows on the plant *Vaccinium*, a member of the heath family. It is mainly grown commercially in northern USA and Canada. A very small production is found in southern Chile, in the Baltic States and in Eastern Europe.

It is quite likely that it was the first Native American fruit eaten in Europe since the ripe berry is noted for its excellent staying power and when shipped across the Atlantic, the cranberry stayed viable for the trip. In fact, sailors nibbled the berry to prevent scurvy on long ocean voyages.

To this day, the cranberry is highly prized in northern Europe, particularly in the Scandinavian countries. Their local version of the berry is called a lingonberry and tastes just a bit spicier than those native to the USA. It is only recently that we in Britain have started singing the cranberry's praises.

As a colour, cranberry is a brilliant vibrant red. As a fresh berry, it's gorgeous to look at, but bite into it and disappointment will be written all over your face. Fresh cranberries are very sour! They are very decorative though. Some people string them round their Christmas trees instead of tinsel. Once, a long time ago, I roasted a whole suckling pig for a New Year's Eve dinner party and gave her a fresh cranberry necklace and earrings.

Sour they may be, but fresh cranberries are definitely your best bet if you want to get the strongest vitamin and antioxidant punch. With a little judicious blending, cranberries can be made into fantastic healthy drinks.

Fresh cranberries are usually available from supermarkets and greengrocers in the autumn and winter. When purchasing them, your eyes are your best guide. The fresh berries should be firm and plump and quite glossy. That high lustre indicates ripeness. Avoid cranberries that are soft and shrivelled. The colour varies from bright to dark red, with the bright red berries being larger and the dark red berries a smaller variety. Store fresh cranberries unwashed but covered in the refrigerator until ready to use. Moisture will hasten spoilage. If you are thinking longer term, cranberries freeze beautifully.

Juices and drinks are available year-round in chiller cabinets and on supermarket shelves. Many cranberry juice products commonly available to consumers, including cranberry juice cocktail, contain only 27% cranberry juice. Twenty-seven per cent is the level shown to be preferred in taste evaluations. A range of light products (which contain low calorie sweeteners) or 100% juice products (which blend cranberry with other naturally sweeter fruit juices such as grape or raspberry) are also available. Additionally, pure cranberry juice (labelled 100% cranberry juice) or cranberry juice concentrates are available in health food stores and can be blended to taste or used for cooking.

CHERRY

A 'bite of the cherry' usually refers to a part of something good. 'Life is just a bowl of cherries' is an expression that means life is pleasant. Cherries have been giving fruit lovers pleasure for centuries. Now the cherry has proved to actually be something more than just a succulent fruit.

According to recent research in the UK and USA, cherry juice can reduce muscle pain and damage induced by exercise.

It has also been discovered that cherries will help relieve the pain associated with arthritis and gout. The anthocyanins in tart cherries offer 10 times the anti-inflammatory relief of aspirin. It has been suggested that a person eating about 20 tart cherries could gain antioxidant or anti-inflammatory benefits.

The chemicals that give tart cherries their red colour may relieve pain better than aspirin and may provide antioxidant protection comparable to commercially available supplements like vitamin E, according to Michigan State University researchers. The new findings 'suggest that the consumption of cherries may have the potential to reduce cardiovascular or chronic diseases in humans (such as arthritis and gout)'.

This research was published in the *Journal of Natural Products* under the aegis of the American Chemical Society, the world's largest scientific society.

So you can either throw a bunch of cherries into a bowl and munch happily away, stone some with a cherry/olive stoner and blend with another fruit of your choice, or if you are feeling lazy, you can buy black cherry concentrate from a natural juice source and dilute with water or combine with another juice.

GRAPE

The 'French Paradox' describes the unexpectedly good heart health among the French despite their typically high-fat diets. A suggested reason is the consumption of red wine, which is made from dark grapes.

Now it turns out that many of the health benefits of red wine can be achieved with a teetotaller's special: grape juice.

Grape juice is pretty much red wine without the alcohol. It doesn't only solve the French Paradox, but also puzzles, riddles, crosswords and other brainteasers. That's because the benefits of grape juice and red wine hit the brain as well as the heart.

The benefits of grape juice to the brain originate from its flavonoids — the natural plant chemicals that act as antioxidants. Antioxidants mop up the harmful free radicals generated when cells burn oxygen for energy and their activity seems to help the brain in two ways. The health of the brain depends on a constant blood flow. Grape juice flavonoids help keep arteries clear by reducing the production of clotting factors while increasing the production of nitric oxide, a substance that keeps arteries open. Flavonoids may also increase the production of 'good' HDL cholesterol and lessen the risk of clogged arteries posed by 'bad' LDL cholesterol. And a recent preliminary study hints that a daily intake of grape juice may even help matters further by reducing blood pressure. The flavonoids that give grapes their health benefits also give them their colour. So research of antioxidant properties has focused on Concord grape juice, made from dark purple Concord grapes.

Concord grape juice turns out to be an even more potent source of antioxidants than the grapes alone. That's because most of the fabulous flavonoids are in the skin and seeds of grapes, and in the process of making red juice or wine, the skin and the seeds stay mixed with the flesh for an extended period of time, allowing the flavonoids to seep into the juice. Since many people don't eat the seeds of grapes, they miss out on many flavonoids even if grapes are part of their daily diet.

We don't see Concord grapes as such in the UK, but we can buy Concord grape juice from concentrate, a treat American children have been drinking for more than 100 years. They don't know it's good for them; they just know they like it.

It's easy to work grape juice into your diet. Since grape juice does contain sugar, you shouldn't drink it as a replacement for water, but rather as a replacement for colas and other soft drinks. A grape juice spritzer, made by mixing juice with sparkling mineral water, makes a refreshing non-alcoholic drink.

You'll get a glassful of heart and brain benefits from either French red wine or red or purple grape juice. Grape juice does have one advantage, though: kids can drink it too.

If you have never had fresh, home-made grape juice, you are missing out; it's not like anything you can buy in a shop. It's more like nectar than store-bought juice, thick and smooth. It can be diluted with still or sparkling water if you don't like that texture.

The recipe on page 110 uses Concord grapes but I'm pretty sure you could use this grape juice recipe with any kind of sweet grape.

WHITE GRAPE

White grapes don't have the same antioxidant punch as red or purple ones, but they do have other documented health benefits.

When my daughters were infants, the first fruit juices introduced into their diets were apple and pear. They didn't have any problem tolerating these juices, but some babies and young children do. Apple and pear juices have a high fructose to glucose ratio and they both contain sorbitol. This can lead to IBS or other gastrointestinal problems. Several studies have shown that children who drink large quantities of these juices have chronic abdominal pain.

Since fruit juice is such an important part of young people's diets, if substituting white grape juice can alleviate these problems, it is certainly worth a try.

For the rest of us, white grapes blended with other fruits, such as peaches or cherries, makes a very delicious drink.

GRAPEFRUIT

Grapefruit makes me happy. I don't really care what colour it is (although my favourite is white). Juicy and tart, with an undercurrent of sweetness, half a grapefruit is my perfect start to every day. Whoever originally named it *Citrus paradisi* got it right! White grapefruit is the most tart, pink grapefruit is sweeter and red grapefruit is the sweetest.

Grapefruits have a rather recent history, having been discovered in Barbados in the 18th century. The grapefruit was first described in 1750 by Griffith Hughes who called it the 'forbidden fruit' of Barbados. Many botanists think the grapefruit was actually the result of a natural cross-breeding which occurred between the orange and the pomelo, a citrus fruit that was brought from Indonesia to Barbados in the 17th century. The resulting fruit was given the name 'grapefruit' in 1814 in Jamaica, a name which reflects the way it's arranged when it grows, hanging in clusters just like grapes.

Grapefruit trees were planted in Florida in the early 19th century, although they did not become a viable commercial crop until later that century. Florida is still a major producer of grapefruits, as is California, Arizona and Texas. Other countries that produce grapefruits commercially include Israel, South Africa and Brazil.

When this new fruit was adopted into cultivation and the name grapefruit came into general circulation, American horticulturists viewed that title as so inappropriate that they endeavoured to have it dropped in favour of 'pomelo'. However, it was difficult to avoid confusion with the other fruit of that name, sometimes called pummelo.
So 'grapefruit' prevailed and is in international use except in Spanish-speaking areas where the fruit is called toronja. In 1962, Florida Citrus Mutual proposed changing the name to something more

appealing to consumers in order to stimulate greater sales. There were so many protests from the public against a name change that the idea was abandoned.

Grapefruit is an excellent source of vitamin C, a vitamin that helps to support the immune system. Vitamin C-rich foods like grapefruit may help reduce cold symptoms or the severity of cold symptoms; over 20 scientific studies have suggested that vitamin C is a cold-fighter. Vitamin C also prevents the free radical damage that triggers the immuno-inflammatory cascade (factors that make up the immune response to infection) and is therefore also associated with reduced severity of inflammatory conditions such as asthma, osteoarthritis and rheumatoid arthritis. As free radicals can oxidise cholesterol and lead to plaques that may rupture causing heart attacks or stroke, vitamin C is beneficial to promoting cardiovascular health. Owing to the multitude of vitamin C's health benefits, it is not surprising that research has shown that consumption of vegetables and fruits high in this nutrient is associated with a reduced risk of death from all causes including heart disease, stroke and cancer. Grapefruit is also a good source of dietary fibre, vitamin A, potassium, folate and vitamin B5. It also contains phytochemicals including liminoids and lycopene.

Choosing to regularly eat lycopene-rich foods, such as pink grapefruit, and drink green tea may greatly reduce a man's risk of developing prostate cancer, suggests research published in the *Asia Pacific Journal of Clinical Nutrition*.

While grapefruit provides many nutrients, the chemicals in grapefruit interfere with the enzymes that metabolise certain drugs in your digestive system. This can result in excessively high levels of these drugs in your blood and an increased risk of serious side effects.

Drugs known to have potentially serious interactions with grapefruit and grapefruit juice include anti-seizure drugs, antidepressants, tranquillisers, calcium channel-blockers (for high blood pressure), HIV medications, statins (to counteract high cholesterol), immunosuppressants, drugs to correct abnormal heart rhythms, erectile dysfunction medications and others. If you are taking any prescription medication, you should check with your GP or pharmacist.

If you find grapefruit juice too tart for your taste, try mixing it with other fruit juices like orange, pineapple, cranberries and other berries.

GUAVA

A member of the myrtle family, guava is cultivated in many tropical and subtropical countries for its edible fruit.

Somewhat pear-shaped, it has a thin, delicate rind and when ripe, it is pale green to gold in some species and pink to red in others. The flesh is creamy white or coral-coloured with many small hard seeds. When the fruit is ripe, it is fragrant and reminiscent at times of apples, passion fruit or strawberries.

Guavas are extremely rich in vitamins A, B and C, with more vitamin C than a typical citrus fruit. Unusually for a fruit, they also contain high levels of calcium.

Although the whole fruit is edible (rind, pulp and seeds), many people choose to discard the centre of the guava, which contains the hard seeds, since the seeds are difficult to separate from the surrounding pulp. The pulp is sweetest and most delicious in the centre, with the outer flesh more tart like an unripe pear. The rind is slightly bitter and rather sour in taste also, but richest in vitamins, with more than five times as much vitamin C as a typical orange.

The fruit is also often prepared in a variety of ways as a dessert. And guava juice has become more popular recently as a result of its nutritional attributes, both on its own and blended with other juices.

My first encounter with guava was as a sort of fruit cheese. A South American colleague once presented me with a block of guava encased in a wooden box. I had no idea what it was or what to do with it. He said that in his country it was traditionally eaten with cream cheese and bland biscuits, often served with drinks before dinner. So I bought the accompaniments and we shared it with a bottle of something. As I remember, it was delicious. The thing is that as we become more and more interested in 'exotic' fruits, their availability increases. Fresh guavas are now sold in our supermarkets and 'guava paste', that fruit cheese I remember from the past, is available from speciality grocers.

KIWI FRUIT

Kiwi fruit owes its name to a native New Zealand bird also called 'kiwi'.

The fruit consists of a hairy, brown peel containing green flesh, with white pulp in the centre, surrounded by black, edible seeds. The fruit has a sweet taste, similar to a mixture of banana, pineapple and strawberry. Despite the name, kiwi fruit is native to China. In fact, in China it is still considered the national fruit.

Kiwi fruit was brought to the Western world at the beginning of the 20th century, when a missionary (the principal of Wanganui Girls' College) introduced it to New Zealand after visiting missions in China.

The very first seed was planted in 1906 by Alexander Allison (a Wanganui nurseryman), and the first fruits were gathered in 1910.

In 1952 the first load of kiwi fruit, 13 tonnes, was exported to England.

In 1958 a fruit-packaging firm in Auckland briefly named the fruit 'melonette', but hastily changed its name to the Maori word 'kiwi' after learning about steep tariffs on melons.

As of 2007, the leading producers of kiwi fruit are: Italy, New Zealand, Chile, France, Greece, Japan and the USA. Kiwi fruit is also cultivated in China, albeit in smaller amounts, in the mountainous regions surrounding the Yangtze River and in the Sichuan province.

Nutrition-wise, kiwi fruit contains about as much potassium as bananas, and also high levels of vitamin C. It is also rich in vitamins A and E, and its black seeds can be crushed to produce kiwi fruit oil, which is very rich in alpha-linoleic acid (an important omega-3 essential fatty acid).

Kiwi fruit contains a substance called actinidin, which has a tenderising effect on foods and is the main cause of an allergy that often manifests itself with itching in the mouth. When adding kiwi fruit to other food, it is generally a good practice to add it just before serving, to prevent actinidin from overly tenderising other foods.

Kiwi fruit is often partnered with strawberries, apples or other fruits when making juices or smoothies.

LEMON

The lemon is indigenous to the northern Indian subcontinent. Trees reached Europe by way of Asia Minor and were first grown in Greece and then Italy. According to Greek mythology, oranges and lemons were a symbol of fecundity and love.

The lemon's travels began in the early Middle Ages on Arab vessels, and it was introduced into Europe near the end of the 12th century. The Crusaders, returning from Palestine, brought citrus fruit trees to plant at home so they could enjoy the taste of the juices that had quenched their thirst during the holy wars. The first lemon groves were cultivated along the Italian Amalfi coast in AD 200, where the climate was ideal. Lemons appeared in Iraq and Egypt by AD 700. They reached Sicily before 1000 and China between 760 and AD 1297. Even back then lemons were prized for their medicinal virtues.

The lemon was closely associated with long sea voyages and slavery, and in 1493 it crossed the Atlantic with Christopher Columbus and arrived in Haiti. According to historical accounts, to protect sailors from the scourge of scurvy which could make a man's teeth fall out in several weeks or kill him if the illness struck too far from land, there was only one remedy: lemon. A writer serving under the French King Louis XIV wrote in his journal that the lemon had to be used whole, together with a good salad of raw onions in order to keep this curse away. (I would think a salad of raw onions would keep everything and everyone away!)

Dr James Lind, a surgeon in the Royal Navy in the mid-18th century, took up this theory again. Cook experimented with the recipe during his second voyage and was proud to have lost only a single man over the course of his long journey.

The humble lemon has magical and wonderful healing powers. Lemons have the highest vitamin C content of any citrus fruit. It is the best prevention for scurvy and is said to counteract the effects of narcotics, soothe sunburn, cure jaundice, reduce temperature, and act as a substitute for quinine. Lemon is most effective for preserving and preventing browning in fruits due to its high citric acid content. Plus, the juice of one lemon supplies 35% of the daily requirement of vitamin C.

Lemon juice in all its forms (fresh, canned, concentrated and frozen, or dehydrated and powdered) is primarily used for old-fashioned lemonade (the non-carbonated kind), in carbonated beverages, or other drinks. It is also used for making pies and tarts, as a flavouring for cakes, cookies, cake icings, puddings, sorbets and ice creams, confectionery, preserves and pharmaceutical products. A few drops of lemon juice, added to cream before whipping, gives stability to whipped cream. A spoonful or two makes soured cream.

Allowing lemons to come to room temperature before squeezing (or heating briefly in a microwave) makes the juice easier to extract.

Some people swear by lemon water (juice diluted with hot water) as a drink to be taken first thing in the morning as a sort of daily detox.

Why this wonderful fruit also became the word for an unsatisfactory person or thing, as in 'that car is such a lemon', I have no idea. But I do think that whoever said 'when life gives us lemons, make lemonade!' had the right idea.

LIME

Limes are small, oval citrus fruits with porous and smooth skin. Lime colour ranges from light to medium green, sometimes with a slight yellow cast. Limes and lemons look similar, but limes are smaller and green (when ripe), and lemons are yellow. Limes are often used to accent the flavours of foods and beverages. The fruits and particularly their juice are used in drinks like limeade, which is akin to lemonade. Lime is a very common ingredient in Mexican, south-western American and Thai dishes. Many alcoholic beverages utilise lime.

Between 1795 and 1815, some 1.6 million gallons (over 7 million litres) of lime juice drastically reduced the mortality rate of seamen. Along with their daily ration of rum, British sailors were required to consume a daily ration of lime juice; which led in time to the nickname 'limey' for all Britons. It was later discovered that this beneficial effect derived from the quantities of vitamin C the fruit contains.

Since Britain was often at war with Mediterranean countries that exported lemons, limes imported cheaply from the English colony of Jamaica were substituted as the citrus of choice.

What we refer to as 'lime' is known as 'Persian lime' or 'Tahiti lime'. There is also a smaller, more aromatic lime about the size of a ping-pong ball called 'key lime'.

Key limes are also known as Mexican lime and West Indies limes. Cultivated for thousands of years in the Indo-Malayan region, this variety has long been treasured for its fruit and decorative foliage.

The key lime made its way to North Africa and the Near East via Arabian traders, and was then carried on to Palestine and Mediterranean Europe by the Crusaders. Columbus is credited with bringing the key lime to Hispaniola (now known as Haiti), where it was taken by Spanish settlers to Florida.

It flourished in south Florida, particularly the Florida Keys, hence the current name. It is most famous for its use in Key Lime Pie made with key lime juice. Its distinctive flavour can be pretty much duplicated by mixing one-half ordinary fresh lime juice with one-half fresh lemon juice. In general, a normal lime is two to three times the size of a key lime.

MANGO

The mango originated in South-East Asia where it has been grown for over 4,000 years. Over the years, mango groves have spread to many parts of the tropical and subtropical world, where the climate allows the mango to grow best.

It has been claimed that more mangos are eaten fresh all over the world than any other fruit. Whether this is true or not, a ripe mango is a wonderful thing to behold! Selecting the ripeness of mangos can be determined by either smelling or squeezing. A ripe mango will have a full, fruity aroma emitting from the stem end. Mangos are ready to eat when slightly soft to the touch and yield to gentle pressure, like a ripe peach. They are best stored at room temperature on a kitchen counter.

Mangos are bursting with protective nutrients. The vitamin content depends upon the variety and maturity of the fruit: when the mango is green, the amount of vitamin C is higher; as it ripens the amount of betacarotene (vitamin A) increases.

A comfort food, mangos really can make you feel better! Beyond being delicious and rich in vitamins, minerals and antioxidants, mangos contain an enzyme with stomach soothing properties similar to the papain found in papayas. These comforting enzymes act as a digestive aid and can be held partially responsible for that feeling of contentment we experience during and after eating a mango. Yes, it is quite natural to crave those mangos!

Some people are defeated when it comes to preparing a mango. The peel is inedible, so it needs to be removed with a small sharp knife. Mangos have a large central stone that precludes halving them or treating them like a peach or nectarine. I think the best way to eat them, frankly, is in the bathtub or over the sink, or wearing protective clothing, because they are awfully messy. If you are eating it in your hand, you can either cut the fruit until you get to the stone, which you should then suck (because that's the best part), or just eat it as you would a peach. It really is worth all the trouble.

However, if you are preparing mangos for a dinner party, or where presentation matters, there are three simple steps to follow:

1. Using a sharp knife, slice the mango lengthways on either side of the stone.
2. Score a criss-cross pattern into the flesh, being careful not to cut through the skin.
3. Gently push out the flesh and place, skin still attached, onto a plate for each diner to cut, or slice off the cubes and discard the skin, then cut the remaining flesh from around the stone into cubes and divide into portions.

As wonderful as mangos are to eat on their own as a fruit, they are quite fantastic in drinks and smoothies, combined with bananas and other fruits.

MANGOSTEEN

I don't think I've ever seen a fresh mangosteen. Describing it from photos, it is a dark purple fruit about the size of a small peach or apple. Despite the name, mangosteens are unrelated to mangos.

The hard rind can be nearly 2.5 cm (1 in) thick. At the centre is the soft opaque white fruit, which resembles a head of garlic but is supposedly sweet and fragrant.

Mangosteen is a tropical fruit that is grown primarily in hot, humid climates of South-East Asia such as Thailand, Malaysia, Singapore, Vietnam and Indonesia.

Records indicate that the first introduction of the mangosteen in the UK goes back to someone named Anton Pantaleon Hove who was dispatched by Sir Joseph Banks to go and try to 'obtain' some better strains of cotton seeds from Gujarat in India. Apparently, amongst his procurements were mangosteen plants that made it back to Plymouth, England in 1789 and which were then moved to Kew. Sir Joseph Banks, whose widespread popularity and renown resulting from his accompanying Captain Cook on his first expedition, was then head of the Royal Botanical Gardens at Kew and president of the Royal Society. Banks was very actively involved throughout this period in guiding, consulting on and sometimes personally funding projects involving both plant and animal introductions. Slowly but surely, the effort was being made to introduce the mangosteen into the western hemisphere. Although there are references to the mangosteen being grown in the UK at some point in history, this no longer is the case.

The mangosteen has been praised for centuries by all who encountered it. The edible interior is renowned for its indescribable sweet-sour melting rush of flavours. But apart from the edible treasure inside the hull, the rind has also been part of Ayurvedic medicine and has been valued for its medicinal qualities. The rind possesses a great diversity of complex organic chemicals amongst which are tannic acid and xanthones. Xanthones comprise much of the promotional health claims for this fruit today and explain why a fruit most of us have never seen is being touted as a wonder food.

Laboratory studies suggest xanthones have anti-cancer effects when they are studied in vitro. Mangosteen has also been found to have anti-inflammatory, antimicrobial, antifungal and antiseptic properties in test-tube studies.

Mangosteen was virtually unknown in the UK until recently. Now both the juice and whole fruit purée are being marketed on the Internet. The excitement about mangosteen beverages may be premature. There are no clinical trials showing that mangosteen extracts have any benefit to humans. What happens in a test tube may not necessarily occur when mangosteen is taken orally.

There are also some concerns about the side effects, which at the present time are unknown, so it would be prudent to approach this fruit carefully, especially if you are taking any medications.

MELON

Melons are a refreshing and versatile fruit that can be served at any time of the day from breakfast to dinner, from starters to desserts. Many melons originated in the Middle East and gradually spread in popularity across Europe. Ancient Egyptians and Romans enjoyed cantaloupes and muskmelons. Melon seeds were transported to the United States by Columbus and eventually cultivated by Spanish explorers in California.

Most people don't know that melons are in the same curcubit family as pumpkins, squashes and cucumbers. Most melons have similar structure to winter squash, with thick flesh and inner seed-filled midsection. The main differences are that pumpkins are considered vegetables and are always cooked, while melons are known as fruits and are almost always served raw.

Melons are a good source of vitamin C and potassium. They have a high water content, are relatively low in calories, and are also fat- and cholesterol-free. There are many varieties of melon. Cantaloupe, honeydew and watermelon are the most well-known types. But sometimes one can find more unusual melons at supermarkets and farmers' markets.

Cantaloupe
What Americans and Britons call a cantaloupe is actually a muskmelon; this familiar fruit with orange flesh and rough netted greenish-coloured skin provides the most betacarotene in the entire melon family. Select melons that are slightly golden with a light fragrant smell (an indication of its ripeness). Cantaloupe is typically available year-round.

Charentais
Charentais is a type of true cantaloupe from France. It has thin, smooth skin with light green stripes, maturing to creamy yellow. Its orange flesh is fine-textured, delightfully scented and very sweet. What makes the charentais melon so special is its superior taste and heady, perfumed aroma.

Gallia
A small, round melon developed in Israel, the skin of the gallia has a bark-like or netted appearance that turns from green to golden-yellow when ripe.

Honeydew
The sweetest of all the melons, larger than the cantaloupe or charentais, honeydew melons have a creamy-yellow rind when ripe and pale green flesh. Although it is sweet, its taste is rather delicate, which perhaps needs to be served with something stronger for contrast.

Ogen
This is a small round hybrid variety named after the kibbutz in Israel where it was first cultivated. It is much admired for its sweet succulence by melon fans.

Watermelon

No other fruit is as synonymous with summer as the watermelon. Now available in Britain, the watermelon is indigenous to Africa. It has rich, red flesh, dark green smooth skin and lots of seeds. Mostly eaten as a thirst quencher in hot weather, the watermelon consists of over 90% water and is greatly beloved by children.

Watermelons were first cultivated in Egypt. The fruit was held in such regard that it was often placed in the tombs of Egyptian kings. They were brought to China around the 10th century and then to the western hemisphere after the discovery of the New World. Today the leading commercial growers are Russia, China, Turkey, Iran and the USA.

Melon is eaten in its natural, raw state. It should be served chilled and is often seasoned with ginger or pepper. It isn't terribly popular as a commercial juice, but it does exist in certain places. It is a favourite among home juicer enthusiasts, usually in combination with other fruits. It is also a marvellous smoothie ingredient.

ORANGE AND TANGERINE

Who doesn't love that glass of wonderful orange liquid that appears on so many breakfast tables around the world? Orange juice – no matter in what form you may consume it – is the most popular fruit juice on the market. Each morning, millions of people begin their day with a glass of refreshing orange juice, and for many families, it's a staple that always has a place of honour in the refrigerator.

Just what attracts people to drink this juice each and every day? For many, it's merely the excellent taste that gets the morning off to a good start. Others enjoy both the good taste and the nutritional advantages that consuming orange juice provides.

It might appear that someone ran out of imagination when it came to naming the orange, even though the fruit is that colour. What if they had called a lime a 'green', an apple a 'red' or a plum a 'purple'? Actually, the name of the colour came from the fruit, first appearing in this sense in the 16th century.

Oranges are the major fruit in the citrus group, accounting for about 70% of citrus output. This group also includes small fruits (such as tangerines, mandarins, clementines and satsumas), lemons and limes, kumquats and grapefruits. The leading processed product in the group is orange juice.

Citrus fruits are produced in many countries around the world, although production shows geographical concentration in certain areas. Mediterranean countries are the leading producers for the international fresh market and Spain plays a dominant role in the area. Most orange juice production is concentrated in only two areas, Sao Paulo in Brazil and Florida in the USA. Brazil is by far the largest orange juice exporter.

Citrus fruits and citrus juices have several beneficial health and nutritive properties. They are rich in vitamin C (ascorbic acid) and folic acid, as well as a good source of fibre. They are fat-free, sodium-free and cholesterol-free. In addition they contain potassium, calcium, folate, thiamine, niacin, vitamin B6, phosphorus, magnesium and copper.

The exact location of the origin of citrus fruits is not clearly identified, although most researchers place it in South-East Asia, at least 4,000 years BC. There are actually, as is often the case, conflicting legends about the origin of citrus. The spread of citrus fruits from Asia to Europe was slow. First, they were taken to North Africa and then, probably by the fall of the Roman Empire, they entered southern Europe, where they flourished in the Middle Ages. Citrus fruits were brought to America by the Spaniards (Columbus took seeds of citrus fruits with him on his second trip – is there anything that isn't accredited to him?)

International trade in fresh citrus fruits began almost two centuries ago. Even at its early stages, Spain held a dominant position in the Mediterranean area, supplying almost all citrus fruits shipped to the UK, Germany and France.

By the 1890s, oranges and orange juice grew in popularity when it was discovered that the fruit contained a wealth of vitamin C.

Global commerce in orange juice only started to increase in the 1940s, after World War II, when citrus processing technologies were invented and developed. Researchers place the beginning of citrus production in Brazil as early as 1530–1540, but the Brazilian citrus industry only started to play a major role in the economy in the 1930s, after the coffee crisis. This growth was particularly high in the 1960s, when the freezes that destroyed an important part of the Florida citrus fields led to increased production in Brazil as an alternative supply area, in order to meet existing orange juice demand in North America and Europe.

During the 1980s Brazil became the largest citrus fruit producer in the world and the first, and almost exclusive, orange juice exporting country. Historically, the United States citrus sector had been more domestically orientated. In the 1990s the citrus industry became more globally integrated.

We now see a plethora of sweet oranges in the UK – navels, the ones that look like they have a belly button and are easy to peel, navelinas, mineolas with a pronounced and distinctive neck, Valencia and Jaffa oranges, mostly for juicing, blood oranges with red flesh, Florida Temple oranges and ortaniques; all of which are excellent for juicing. Then there is the Seville – a bitter orange mostly used here to make marmalade. It can also be juiced, but it is perhaps better utilised in marinades than as a fruit juice.

In addition to the many types of orange on the market today, there are also different varieties of tangerine: the original, a small sweet orange containing numerous pips, and two hybrids: the clementine and the satsuma. The clergyman Pierre Clement crossed a mandarin and an orange and the result was a seedless mandarin with a looser skin, making it easier to peel – the clementine. The Satsuma is a Japanese hybrid. It is similar to the tangerine in taste and appearance, but it contains no pips.

PAPAYA

Papayas, native to Central America, have long been revered by the Latin American Indians. Spanish and Portuguese explorers brought papayas to many other subtropical lands to which they journeyed, including

India, the Philippines and parts of Africa. Deliciously sweet with musky undertones and a soft, butter-like consistency, the papaya was supposedly called the 'fruit of the angels' by Christopher Columbus and no wonder. Once considered quite exotic, they can now be found in supermarkets throughout the year. Although there is a slight seasonal peak in early summer and autumn, papaya trees produce fruit all year round.

Papayas are spherical or pear-shaped fruits that can be as long as 50 cm (20 inches). The ones commonly found in the market usually average about 18 cm (7 inches) and weigh about 450 g (1 lb). Their flesh is a rich orange colour with either yellow or pink hues. Inside the inner cavity of the fruit are black, round seeds encased in a gelatinous-like substance. The papaya's seeds are edible, although their peppery flavour is somewhat bitter. The fruit, as well as the other parts of the papaya tree, contains papain, an enzyme that helps digest proteins. This enzyme is especially concentrated in the fruit when it is unripe. Papain is extracted to make digestive enzyme dietary supplements and meat tenderiser, and is also used as an ingredient in some chewing gums. The riper the papaya, the greater the antioxidant value.

The flesh of ripe papayas has a smooth and creamy texture that is often so rich that it needs to be diluted with another liquid or water unless that thickness is desired. Hence, it is a wonderful ingredient for smoothies where that creamy texture is a plus.

PASSION FRUIT

According to the Passionfruit Growers Association in New Zealand, 'Fresh passion fruit, with its yellow polka dotted flesh, brings together flavours of different fruits and makes them sing a different song, adds an exotic tingle to individual fruits or makes a salad come alive.'

The purple passion fruit (*Passiflora edulis*) is a native of the rainforest margins in the Amazon region of Brazil and perhaps also of Paraguay and northern Argentina. It has adapted to the cooler subtropics and the high altitude tropics.

Before you start thinking of passion fruit as an aphrodisiac, the word 'passion' has a religious rather than sexual background. Passion fruit acquired its name from Spanish missionaries who thought parts of the plant's flower resembled different religious symbols. The Jesuit missionaries who accompanied the Conquistadors to South America saw in its striking flower a means of illustrating the Crucifixion; the 10 petals and sepals represented the apostles, the crown of thorns was seen in the filaments, the five anthers represent the five wounds, the three stigmas were allied with the nails used to pierce the hands and feet of Jesus and the vine's tendrils were equated to the whips.

While some people sing the praises of the fruit, I am very partial to the juice, which I think is sublime, especially mixed with cranberry juice or apple and carrot juice. If you are juicing passion fruit at home, extract the juice from the pulp by liquidising the pulp at a very low speed (this stops the chipping of the seeds, which turn out as black specks in the juice; they are very hard to remove and look like dirt) for about one minute. Tip the contents into a muslin cloth and squeeze out the juice leaving the seeds behind. Liquidise the juice only, at high speed; this reduces the particle size and helps to reduce settling in the final product.

PEACH AND NECTARINE

Although its botanical name, *Prunus persica*, suggests the peach is native to Persia, it actually originated in China where it has been cultivated since the early days of Chinese culture. Peaches were mentioned in Chinese writings as far back as the 10th century BC and were a favoured fruit of emperors. The peach is a symbol of longevity and good luck in China.

Its English name derives from the Latin plural of *persicum malum*, meaning Persian apple. In Middle English, it melded into *peche*, the French word for peach and much closer to what we call it today.

The Persians brought the peach from China and passed it on to the Romans. It was brought to the United States by Spanish explorers in the 16th century and eventually made it to England and France in the 17th century, where it was a popular, albeit rare, treat.

In Queen Victoria's day, no meal was complete without a fresh peach presented in a fancy cotton napkin.

Various American Indian tribes are credited with migrating the peach tree across the United States, taking seeds along with them and planting them as they wandered the country.

Although Thomas Jefferson had peach trees at Monticello, US farmers did not begin commercial production until the 19th century in Maryland, Delaware, Georgia and finally Virginia. Although the Southern states lead in the commercial production of peaches, they are also grown in California, Michigan and Colorado.

Today, peaches are the second largest commercial fruit crop in the USA, second only to apples. Italy, China and Greece are also major producers of peaches.

The nectarine is a cultivar group of peach with a smooth skin. Though fuzzy peaches and nectarines are regarded commercially as different fruits, with nectarines often erroneously thought to be a crossbreed between peaches and plums, or a 'peach with a plum skin', they belong to the same species as peaches. Several genetic studies have concluded in fact that nectarines are created due to a recessive gene, whereas a fuzzy peach skin is dominant.

As with peaches, nectarines can be white or yellow, and clingstone or freestone. On average, nectarines are slightly smaller and sweeter than peaches, but with much overlap. The lack of skin fuzz can make nectarine skins appear more reddish than those of peaches, contributing to the fruit's plum-like appearance. The lack of down also means their skin is more easily bruised than that of peaches.

The history of the nectarine is unclear: the first recorded mention in English is from the 17th century, but they were probably grown much earlier in central and eastern Asia.

Normal peach trees occasionally produce a few nectarines, and vice versa. Charles Darwin noticed that peach trees spontaneously produced nectarines and that this also happened the other way around. He even described a tree that produced a fruit that was half-peach, half-nectarine, and later fell back to producing peaches.

Peaches are not fully ripe when they arrive in the shops. Most will be ready to eat in two to three days if stored at room temperature. If you are in a rush for your peach juice, enclosing them in a paper bag to trap the natural gasses can speed up ripening.

When looking for good peaches to juice, look for fruit that are firm and full-coloured and avoid ones that are tinged with green; the green areas won't ripen properly. Make sure you remember to remove the stone!

Some may find fresh peach juice a bit thick. If this is the case, either dilute it in a multi-juice recipe or add water or apple juice.

PEAR

Pears are one of the world's oldest cultivated and beloved fruits. In 5000 BC, Feng Li, a Chinese diplomat, abandoned his responsibilities when he became obsessed with grafting peaches, almonds, persimmons, pears and apples as a commercial venture. In *The Odyssey*, the Greek poet laureate Homer lauds pears as a 'gift of the gods'.

Thanks to their versatility and long storage life, pears were a valuable and much-desired commodity among the trading routes of the ancient world.

In the 17th century a great flourishing of modern pear variety cultivation began in Europe. And in popular culture, the pear tree was immortalised alongside a partridge in the 18th-century Christmas carol, *The Twelve Days of Christmas*.

Pears are the fleshy fruit of a tree widely grown in most parts of the world, except the tropics. Many different varieties of dessert and cooking pear are grown and marketed in Britain and large numbers are also imported. Some are very juicy and sweet, and when absolutely ripe they make an excellent dessert fruit, but if they are allowed to become overripe, the texture and taste are greatly compromised.
Pears ripen from the end of summer to the beginning of winter and some types will keep until Christmas. They should be stored well apart, on wooden shelves, in a temperature of 4–16°C (40–60°F). The English dessert pear must be watched carefully and eaten as soon as it is ripe, when it should yield to slight pressure at the stalk end.

The most common and popular pear grown in the UK is Conference, but my very favourite is the succulent Comice, usually seen in the shops around Christmas time. Many other varieties may also be found in supermarkets, farm shops and farmers' markets.
If you have a fruit-bearing pear tree in your garden with a glut of pears, you are probably already making juice or perry (pear cider). A branded perry known as Babycham, marketed principally as a woman's drink and sold in miniature champagne-style bottles, was once popular but has now become unfashionable.

Pears contain antioxidants and no fat, with health benefits from vitamin A, vitamin B1, vitamin B2, vitamin C, niacin, and the minerals calcium, phosphorus, iron and potassium.

PINEAPPLE

Pineapples (*Ananas comosus*) are native to southern Brazil and Paraguay, but after the colonisation of the New World, they were rapidly transported to all areas of the tropics. They are now widely grown in tropical and subtropical areas with moderate temperatures, such as islands just inside the tropics and on the eastern side of continents. The major producing areas include Hawaii, Brazil, Malaysia, the Philippines and the Ivory Coast.

On his second voyage to the New World in 1493, Columbus and his crew encountered a fruit that they had never seen before on the Caribbean island of Guadeloupe. One of them described it as being 'in the shape of a pine cone, twice as big, which fruit is excellent and it can be cut with a knife, like a turnip and it seems to be wholesome'. Its resemblance to a pine cone gave rise to the fruit's English name of pineapple, while its Latin name *ananas* came from the word 'nana' which was the local people's name for the plant. People in the Caribbean at that time valued the fruit highly, placing it outside their homes to welcome visitors. Later, Europeans adopted this habit with the pineapple motif used on gateposts and in carvings.

When various explorers brought pineapples back to Europe, attempts were made to cultivate the sweet, prized fruit until it was realised that the fruit's need for a tropical climate inhibited its ability to flourish in that region. By the end of the 16th century, Portuguese and Spanish explorers introduced pineapples into many of their Asian, African and South Pacific colonies, countries in which the pineapple is still being grown today.

Since pineapples are very perishable, and modes of transportation to bring them stateside from the Caribbean Islands were relatively slow centuries ago, fresh pineapples were a rarity that became coveted by the early American colonists. While glazed, sugar-coated pineapples were a luxurious treat, it was the fresh pineapple itself that became the sought-after true symbol of prestige and social class. In fact, the pineapple, because of its rarity and expense, was such a status item in those times that all a party hostess had to do was to display the fruit as part of a decorative centrepiece, and she would be awarded more than just a modicum of social awe and recognition.

In the 18th century, pineapples began to be cultivated in Hawaii, the only state in the USA in which they are still grown. In addition to Hawaii, countries that grow pineapples commercially include Thailand, the Philippines, China, Brazil and Mexico.

Pineapple contains the enzyme bromelain, which digests food by breaking down protein. Pineapple juice can thus be used as a marinade and meat tenderiser.

Some old wives' tales claim that pineapple has benefits for some intestinal disorders; others maintain that it helps to induce childbirth when a baby is overdue.

Pineapple is a good source of manganese as well as containing significant amounts of vitamin C and vitamin B1.

Pineapples have exceptional juiciness and a vibrant tropical flavour that balances the tastes of sweet and tart. Although the season for pineapple runs from March through to June, they are available year-round in local supermarkets.

Miraculously, although pineapple is a tropical fruit, it has even been known to grow in the UK. Pineapple is one of the world's most unique and exotic tropical fruits, yet it is possible to cultivate it in a temperate zone under controlled conditions, with the most difficult part of the process just getting it rooted. There are photos on the Internet of a pineapple successfully grown in Surrey! This could become a fun family project for the kids.

Fresh pineapple is a great juice on its own or a good addition to other juices and smoothies. It is very easy to peel, especially if you have a pineapple corer/slicer, which works like a corkscrew. A friend gave me one years ago and I thought it was the silliest gadget I had ever seen until I used it. It works a treat!

POMEGRANATE

The pomegranate is an ancient fruit with a rich history. A native of Persia, it has always been an important part of the Middle Eastern diet. Until recently, however, pomegranates were something of a seasonal novelty in the West. Then medical studies suggested what the ancients believed and Middle Easterners probably take for granted: pomegranates are really good for you.

One of the earliest cultivated fruits, the pomegranate has been traced back as far as 3000 BC. Some scholars even suggest that it was a pomegranate not an apple that tempted Eve.

In their long history, pomegranates have been linked to health, fertility and rebirth. They figure prominently in many religions and are found in art and literature.

King Tutankhamun and other Ancient Egyptians were buried with pomegranates in hope of a second life. The fruits are said to have been a favourite of the prophet Muhammad, and in Islam the gardens of paradise contain pomegranates.

In the Judaeo-Christian Bible, Moses tells the Israelites they are going to a land of pomegranates (among other things.) Paintings often show the Virgin Mary or the infant Jesus holding a pomegranate. The Greek goddess Persephone's taste for the pomegranate resigned her to several months a year in the underworld.

Pomegranates are mentioned in Homer's *Odyssey*, and Juliet tells Romeo the night is young since it is the nightingale – and not the lark – that is 'singing in yon pomegranate tree'.

Scientists say the leathery-skinned, orange-sized fruit with the sweet-tart juice may help fight heart disease, cancer and problems associated with ageing. It's loaded with antioxidants, vitamins, potassium, folic acid and iron. Pomegranates are the new superfood on the throne of well-being. For home use, the whole fruit or seeds can be refrigerated in plastic bags or the seeds can be frozen separately.

The popularity of pomegranates may have been delayed in the West because it is such a labour-intensive fruit. Beneath its tough but thin skin, each pomegranate holds hundreds of tiny seeds encased in translucent ruby pulp. Bitter, inedible membranes hold the seeds, and getting the seeds out can be a struggle. Since the pomegranate's health profile has risen, though, more people are willing to make the effort. I remember pomegranates fondly from my early youth (we called them Chinese apples). Thankfully, my mother knew what to do with them, so they provided my cousin and I with hours of fun around Halloween time.

A ripe, ready-to-eat pomegranate is a luscious jewel of a fruit, capable of transforming any meal into an extraordinary experience. And although this delicious fruit may seem exotic, it's wonderfully easy to enjoy. There are many ways to remove the seeds from a pomegranate. One is to cut the crown end off the pomegranate and then lightly score the skin from top to bottom in quarters. Immerse the fruit in a bowl of cool water and soak for a minute or two. Hold the fruit under water (which prevents juice from spattering) and break sections apart. Next, separate the seeds from the rind and membrane. Seeds will sink to the bottom of the bowl; rind and membrane will float. Skim off and discard the rind and membrane. Drain seeds, then pat dry. (At some markets, you can buy containers of seeds that someone else has extracted.) Simmer pomegranate seeds in water to cover till soft, then press out the juice through a sieve, add an equal amount of sugar, and simmer for 10 minutes to make a syrup. (Cool and store in a bottle.) Sprinkle pomegranate seeds on Middle Eastern dishes such as hummous, baba ghanoush and rice pilaf.

How to Juice a Pomegranate
This only requires a manual citrus juicer. All you have to do is cut the pomegranates in half, put them on the juicer and squeeze and press until no more juice is released. Repeat with remaining pomegranates. Line a fine sieve with muslin and strain the juice through it. Add sugar to taste.

Alternatively, warm the fruit slightly and roll it between your hands to soften. Cut a hole in the stem end and place it over a glass. Let the juice run out, squeezing the fruit to extract it. In addition to drinking pomegranate juice as is, it is a wonderful enhancement to lemonade.

PRUNE

Sweet, with a deep taste and a sticky chewy texture, prunes are not only fun to eat but are also highly nutritious. Prunes are a good source of vitamin A, fibre, potassium and copper. As with other dried fruits, they are available all year round.

Unfortunately for the delicious and quite beneficial prune, its name has acquired a somewhat negative connotation, being associated with wrinkles, old age and sluggish gastrointestinal tracts. So, to give prunes some PR that may help overcome this stigma and to promote prunes to their rightful place in the American diet, they have been informally christened with another name, a name that reflects their heritage . . . the 'dried plum'. They are still called prunes everywhere else.

California produces more prunes than the rest of the world combined. Approximately 99% of the US supply and 60% of the world's supply comes from California. The process of drying plums to make prunes is thought to have originated thousands of years ago in an area near the Caspian Sea, the same region where the prune-producing European plums originated. It spread throughout Europe with the migration of different cultures and civilisations.

The process of drying plums to produce prunes took hold in California in the mid-19th century during the

Gold Rush when brothers Louis and Pierre Pellier brought the Petite d'Agen plum from France and grafted it onto wild American rootstock. Thanks to its high sugar content, the Petite d'Agen ripens fully on the tree without fermenting around the stone.

This story may be apocryphal, but when a labour shortage hit California in 1905, a farmer turned to 500 monkeys to harvest the prune plums. Organised into gangs of 50 with a human foreman, the monkeys picked the prune plums well, but ate them all up! Today, machines do the work – without eating the fruit.

There's also an urban legend that the soft drink, Dr Pepper, contains prune juice. This is just a myth. The company is adamant that it doesn't and never did.

There are several ways to make your own prune juice. Some people advocate cooking the prunes, then mashing them and blending with water, but the easiest method is to soak 450 g (1 lb) of stoned prunes in 1 litre (1¾ pints) of filtered water for 24 hours or more, and then purée in a blender or food processor.

RASPBERRY

Most likely native to Asia, wild raspberries have been eaten since prehistoric times. The Crusaders wrote poems about the delicious fruit with the heady perfume they found on their way to Jerusalem. Cultivation began in England and France, probably in the 1600s. By the 18th century cookery writers were devising recipes using the fruit for raspberry wine and vinegar, sweets and jams. Raspberries were also used as a cure for sore eyes and throats and to cleanse the teeth. In North America, raspberries were considered a luxury well into the mid-1800s.

Scotland is famous for its raspberry growing. Due to the difficulties of growing strawberries in a cooler climate, a group of market gardeners in Angus in the early 20th century set up a cooperative of raspberry growers, which ultimately led to Tayside becoming the most important UK raspberry-growing region, producing 80% of the commercial crop. The long hours of summer daylight and relatively dry summers allow the fruit to mature slowly, providing a well-flavoured berry.

In the late 1950s raspberries were taken from Scotland to Covent Garden on a steam train known as the Raspberry Special.

Raspberries are also grown on farms throughout the UK. For the local raspberry-lover, 'Pick your own' farms abound during the summer, providing a fun way of getting hold of the freshest fruit.

Raspberries are rich in vitamin C and contain ellagic acid, a potential anti-cancer agent. They are a source of fibre and may lower high blood cholesterol levels. They are also very low in calories, and if they are properly ripe you may not need to add sugar to them, so you can throw wanton handfuls into juice and smoothie mixtures without guilt.

One of the most common but serious afflictions in young children, gastroenteritis, could be prevented with simple raspberry juice, it seems. Laboratory experiments in New South Wales showed that a range of common stomach bugs such as e. coli are actually killed off by raspberry juice or raspberry juice cordial diluted to as low as 10% strength. Human trials are now being planned to try and prove that routinely drinking raspberry juice could act as a preventative against outbreaks of stomach infections in places like schools or for children and adults while travelling.

When buying or picking raspberries, choose berries that do not have cores in them. If they have cores, they were picked too early and are likely to be too tart.

To make raspberry juice from scratch, simmer them as follows: use equal parts of raspberries to water. Once they are simmering, mash with a fork and cook for about 10 minutes to draw out the flavour. Set aside to cool. Strain the liquid in a muslin-lined sieve, gather the muslin ends together and squeeze until all the juice is extracted. Measure the liquid and cook it again with 1 part caster sugar to 4 parts juice, or to taste.

You can also save the unsweetened juice for later use by measuring with a liquid measure into 240 ml (8 fl oz) quantities. Put into zip-lock freezer bags. Then place all the bags into one large bag and freeze. This will preserve the vitamins in the juice. Since it is already measured, you will know how much sugar to add to whatever it is you are making. Another use for the unsweetened juice is to add about 120 ml (4 fl oz) to a pitcher of fresh lemonade or cold sweetened iced tea for a fantastic summer drink.

STRAWBERRY

The fragrantly sweet juiciness and deep red colour of strawberries can brighten up both the taste and aesthetics of any meal; it is no wonder they are the most popular berry fruit in the world, adored by both children and adults.

Strawberries boast more vitamin C than any other berry; 60 g (2 oz) provides 70% of the recommended daily requirement. They also, like raspberries, contain ellagic acid, which research suggests could help to prevent some types of cancer.

As I wrote in my *Berries* book, British strawberries are the best in the world. I prefer to eat them just as they are. However, they are very successful as juice, if a bit thick-textured, and delightful in smoothies. Good quality strawberries are also sweet enough not to require extra sugar. However, in June 2003, *The Guardian* printed a Heston Blumenthal recipe for strawberry juice that does use sweetened strawberries and is well worth looking up and trying because it is delicious.

Although allergic reactions can occur to virtually any food, research studies on food allergy consistently report more problems with some foods than with others. It turns out that strawberries are one of the foods most commonly associated with allergic reactions. But a number of people who are allergic to eating strawberries find that they can tolerate them as juice. It is worth talking to an allergist if you have this problem.

From the Hungry Monster.com website, I learned two things about strawberries:

In medieval times strawberries were regarded as an aphrodisiac and soup made of strawberries, borage and soured cream was traditionally served to newlyweds at their wedding breakfast.

It is an Ancient Egyptian myth that if you eat 300 strawberries in one hour you will turn into an evil cat. If I ate 300 strawberries in one hour, I would probably get a terrible rash and feel quite ill, so the evil cat might be preferable!

FRUIT NECTAR

Fruit nectar is fruit juice with water and sugar or honey and fruit pulp or purée added, so it tastes like a thicker version of sweetened juice. Fruit nectars can either be single flavours or flavour blends. In the commercially prepared nectars, up to 20% of the total weight of the product can be sugar or honey, so if you are watching your calorie intake, you would be better off either making your own or sticking with juice.

A very simple unsweetened recipe for fruit nectar can be found on page 110.

VEGETABLE
JUICES

BEETROOT

Beetroot (*Beta vulgaris*) evolved from wild sea beet, a native of coastlines from India to Britain and the ancestor of all cultivated forms of beet.

Sea beet was first grown in the eastern Mediterranean and Middle East – although it was only the leaves that were eaten at that time. The root was carrot-shaped and the Romans were, at first, mainly interested in it as a medicine. The first recipes for preparing the roots appeared in the 3rd century AD and were used mainly for curative broths to treat fevers and other ailments.

The Romans considered beetroot an aphrodisiac (it's rich in the mineral boron which is important in the production of human sex hormones). The belief persists to this day that if a man and a woman eat from the same beetroot, they will fall in love (with each other, presumably).

The rounded root shape that we are familiar with today wasn't developed until the 16th century and became widely popular in Central and Eastern Europe a couple of hundred years later. Many of the classic beetroot dishes originated in this region, including the most famous beetroot soup, known as borscht.

After World War II, pickled beetroot in bottles was the most widely available form, but the vinegars were often strong and harsh – enough to put many people off beetroot for life! More recently, smaller, more tender 'baby' summer-grown beetroots have been developed.

Beetroot is a powerhouse of nutrients. Just three baby beetroot equals one of your five-a-day. It is a rich source of carbohydrates, a good source of protein, and has high levels of important vitamins, minerals and micronutrients. It is virtually fat free and low in calories. It is also a good source of potassium and magnesium.

Beetroot contains fibre, which can help reduce blood cholesterol. It also contains carotenoids and flavonoids, which help prevent LDL or 'bad' cholesterol from being oxidised and deposited in the arteries. It's an excellent source of folic acid and is therefore recommended to women who are pregnant or planning to become pregnant. Cooked beetroot is a great source of folate that may protect you against high blood pressure, Alzheimer's and dementia. It is also crucial to the development of a baby's spinal cord during the first three months of pregnancy as a good intake of folate helps to prevent spinal cord defects such as spina bifida.

Betalins are a type of antioxidant found in beetroot in fairly large quantities. You don't need to eat much beetroot to take in a beneficial amount of betalin.

Beetroot contains betaine, a substance that relaxes the mind and is used to treat depression. It also contains trytophan (also found in chocolate!) which contributes to a sense of well-being.

With all of this good stuff going on with beetroot, there must be a downside, right? Don't be alarmed, if after eating beetroot, there are pink side effects! It's the red pigment in beetroot that passes harmlessly through the digestive system. Unless you know better, you might think you are bleeding rectally.

Many people are averse to beetroot having only experienced crinkle-cut slices steeped in overpowering vinegar. This is a shame because fresh beetroot has much to commend it in terms of flavour (sweet, slightly earthy), texture (smooth and velvety) and colour (dark red/purple, or an appealingly lurid pink when combined with cream or yoghurt).

These attributes make it a key ingredient in many fabulous salads. And if you haven't tried fresh beetroot juice you may be pleasantly surprised at how subtle it is, particularly when offset with a sharper ingredient such as orange or apple. You should also consider juicing the greens for an even healthier drink.

CARROT

The idiom 'carrot and stick' refers to combining a promised reward with a threatened penalty, the carrot being the reward.

The bright orange fleshy root vegetable we know and love today as the carrot is a far cry from its wild ancestor, a small tough, pale-fleshed acrid root plant. Probably no one would be eating carrots that were once small, very thin, red, purple and even black taproots with a distasteful bitterness if no one had taken an interest in improving their flavour. Luckily, some motivated Dutch people took carrots under their horticultural wings and taught them how to be sweet. It's a long story.

Carrots were originally purple or red, with a thin root. The species did not turn orange until the 1500s when Dutch agricultural scientists and growers used a mutant yellow carrot seed from North Africa to develop a carrot in the colour of the House of Orange, the Dutch Royal Family. In an attempt to 'nationalise' the country's favourite vegetable they began experiments on improving the pale yellow versions by cross-breeding them with red varieties. These varieties contain betacarotene to produce orange-coloured roots. This was developed to become the dominant species across the world.

Carrots store a goldmine of nutrients. The carrot is a herbaceous plant containing about 87% water, rich in mineral salts and vitamins. No other vegetable or fruit contains as much carotene as carrots, which the body converts to vitamin A. This is a truly versatile vegetable and an excellent source of vitamins B and C as well as calcium pectate, an extraordinary pectin fibre that has been found to have cholesterol-lowering properties. Raw carrots are an excellent source of vitamin A and potassium; they contain vitamin C, vitamin B6, thiamine, folic acid and magnesium.

Are carrots more nutritious in their raw state than when cooked? That's a very good question. Opinions vary. Clearly a carrot has more goodness in it when it is raw; therefore you would assume that is the healthiest way to eat it. But unless the carrot is juiced first, then consumed, the body cannot break down the goodness because of the cellular nature of the carrot.

Can eating carrots really improve your eyesight? Sorry no! They will help to keep your eyes healthy and not deteriorate as quickly. When your mother said 'Eat your carrots, they'll help your eyes', she had a point. Eating carrots does provide benefits to your eyes, experts say. Both vitamin A and betacarotene are known to lower the risk of eye disease, hence the carrot's association with eyesight. They do help you see in the dark, but can only improve your night vision if you are deficient in vitamin A.

If you need any more reasons for drinking carrot juice, there is one obvious one – it is absolutely delicious. Do not overdose – your skin will turn yellow – it's called carotenemia! Consume too many carrots or drink too much juice and your skin, mostly the hands, will turn yellowish-orange. There are two possible reasons why this happens. Either your body is unable to process all the carotene properly in the carrot juice you are drinking, or your liver is toxic. Either way, the colour shows up in your skin. This phenomenon is uncommon in healthy adults because their livers should function well enough to convert the betacarotene to vitamin A and eliminate the rest from the body. As a rule, spinach juice won't turn you green, beetroot won't turn you red, carrots won't turn you orange. We usually get yellow/orange when we are jaundiced because our liver is congested or it is casting off toxins.

CELERY

The celery that we know today was derived from a wild plant. While thought to have its origins in the Mediterranean regions of northern Africa and southern Europe, it was also native to areas extending east to the Himalayas. Wild celery differed a bit from its modern day counterpart in that it featured less stalks and more leaves.

Celery has a long and prestigious history of use, first as a medicine and then later as a food. The initial mention of the medicinal properties of celery leaves dates back to the 9th century BC, when celery made an appearance in the *Odyssey*, the famous epic by the Greek poet, Homer. The Ancient Greeks used the leaves as laurels to decorate their renowned athletes, while the Ancient Romans used it as a seasoning, a tradition that has carried on through the centuries.

It was not until the Middle Ages that celery's use expanded beyond medicine and seasoning into consideration as a food. And while today, for most people, thoughts of celery conjure up images of cheese platters, eating this delicious crunchy vegetable raw did not really become popular until the 18th century in Europe. Celery was introduced into the United States early in the 19th century.

Celery is high in magnesium, iron and chlorophyll, which is an excellent blood builder, and is one of the richest sources of organic sodium.

Celery juice is thought to be a superb nerve tonic. Celery juice on its own tastes a little bitter so it is usually mixed with carrots or apples.

The strong diuretic (water removing) powers of celery enable it to be used in the control of health problems such as arthritis and rheumatism. Sufferers may consume the vegetable cooked or raw, or in juice form which is the most health effective treatment of all. For a dieter, a tablespoonful of honey in celery juice, sipped slowly, will very effectively reduce the appetite if taken before a meal and makes a delightful drink.

The same mixture, taken as a nightcap, will help you to relax into a soothing and restful sleep. There are claims that those who in the past have suffered from a tendency towards gallstones or kidney stones usually find that these painful deposits do not form again if they drink celery juice. It seems likely that this effect is related to the anti-arthritic properties of the juice.

With regard to seasoning, celery is great for adding a salty taste to vegetable juices. Do you have a headache? Drink a glass of celery juice. Even the Ancient Greeks used celery for the universal problem of headaches. Do you live in the air-polluted inner city? Celery/apple juice can cleanse the body of carbon dioxide. In hot weather, celery juice cools down the body. Do you have a problem with muscle cramps and fatigue during workouts? The potassium/sodium balance in celery juice will be a great asset. Always leave the celery leaves on for juicing, but juice the celery last because it is stringy and tends to clog the juice machine.

Thanks to the plant's cellular structure, its ingestion can result in negative calories, but it is a fallacy to believe that this has anything to do with the energy expended in chewing. Though chewing may feel strenuous, it burns about the same amount of energy as watching paint dry. It is our bodily energy trying to digest the celery that exhausts the calories. A cold, low-calorie drink would enhance this effect because the liquid needs to be warmed to body temperature, which requires a further expenditure of energy. This won't make you lose any weight because the expenditure of energy is very small. On the other hand, in defence of celery as a 'diet food', if you are eating or drinking celery, you aren't eating chocolate at the same time! Celery juice also helps curb the craving for sweets.

When buying celery, look for firm, solid bunches with bright green leaves.

CUCUMBER

The saying 'as cool as a cucumber' originates from the fact that the internal temperature of cucumbers is about 10°C (20°F) lower than the temperature of the air on a hot day. People living in the Middle East and India have been eating cucumbers for hundreds of years as a natural coolant.

The flesh of cucumbers is primarily composed of water, but also contains ascorbic acid (vitamin C) and caffeic acid, both of which help soothe skin irritations and reduce swelling. The hard skin of the cucumber is rich in fibre and contains a variety of beneficial minerals including silica, potassium and magnesium.

The silica in cucumber is an essential component of healthy connective tissue, which includes muscles, tendons, ligaments, cartilage and bone. Cucumber juice is often recommended as a source of silica to improve the complexion and health of the skin from within, plus cucumber's high water content makes it naturally hydrating - a must for glowing skin. Cucumbers are also used topically for various types of skin problems, including swelling under the eyes and sunburn. That's why you often see photos of people in health spas with cucumber slices on their eyelids.
As a beauty treatment, grated cucumber applied over the face, eyes and neck for 15–20 minutes has been

found effective as a tonic for facial skin. It gives elasticity to the skin, which results in a more youthful complexion. Its regular use also aids in the treatment of pimples, blackheads, wrinkles and dryness. As a hair tonic, cucumber juice promotes hair growth due to its high silicon and sulphur content, particularly when mixed with carrot, lettuce and spinach juice.
For drinking purposes, cucumber juice is usually mixed with other juices.

When buying cucumbers for juicing, look for non-waxed varieties, which allow you to juice the cucumber in its skin. Look for firm cucumbers with a dark green, wrinkle-free skin. They will keep well in the refrigerator for several days. If you do not use the entire cucumber during one meal or beauty treatment, wrap the remainder tightly in clingfilm or place it in a sealed container.

LEAFY GREEN VEGETABLES

Cabbage, Kale, Lettuce, Spinach

> 'It's not easy being green'
> Kermit the Frog, *Sesame Street*

We all know that green vegetables are an important part of a healthy diet, but somehow, children have an inbuilt dislike of them. So it's not easy getting them to eat green things.

Green juices are a great way to get the greens into your diet. The difference between smoothies and juices is fibre – juices have no fibre, whereas smoothies have ALL of the fibre, but if you find smoothies too bulky or thick, or you just don't like them, then juicing is a great alternative. The secret to a good green juice is to work with one–three strong green leaves such as kale, spinach, watercress, parsley, wheatgrass, etc., then add milder vegetables such as cucumber, celery or lettuce for more liquid and extra vitamins and minerals, and if you feel your juice needs sweetening or sharpening, add a little apple, pear, carrot, red pepper, lemon or lime. There's nothing like a green juice for lifting your energy and mind, especially first thing in the morning. Don't forget, to juice greens you need a juicer that is capable of handling them (see page 14).

When you mix green juice with pineapple, be sure to drink it straight away, as the bromelain in the pineapple will begin to digest the protein from your greens. But if there will be a lapse from the time you make your juice to the time you drink it, e.g. you are taking your drink to work for lunch, simply keep the two juices separate until you are ready to use them and mix when you are ready.

ONION

Though not as steeped in lore and superstition as it's more odoriferous cousin, garlic, the onion has enjoyed some regard through the ages.

The Ancient Egyptians used onions as currency and gave them prominent places in the tombs of pharaohs, including the eye sockets of Rameses IV (ouch!).

The original Olympian athletes ate onions to balance the blood.

Roman gladiators were rubbed down with onion juice for increased strength.

Charlemagne liked them so much he ordered them to be planted in the royal garden.

Onions have manifold health benefits. If you have a chesty cough, onion juice mixed with ginger juice and honey acts as an expectorant. Similarly, onion juice mixed with ginger juice, black pepper and salt helps in controlling asthma and problems of the throat, tonsils and lungs. There are some people who swear that eating raw onions or applying onion juice to the forehead helps to control the symptoms of a cold. Since the iron content in onions is high and is easily assimilated, onions may also play a part in treating anaemia. It is also maintained that a regular intake of onions maintains normal blood circulation and helps to prevent heart disease. While all of this may come under the category of folk medicine, there is no reason to believe that it may not be true.

For whatever reason you are using onions, it is very powerful. If you are not using onions for any particular therapeutic purpose, when juicing you should use very little and always mix with other vegetables.

PARSLEY

Parsley is perhaps one of the most commonly used but therapeutically underrated of herbs. How often does one see a dish in a restaurant garnished with parsley, and the waiter leaves the parsley on the serving dish, or the customers reject it as mere decoration? If they knew how good it was for them, they would ask for more.

Parsley contains more vitamin C than any other standard culinary fruit or vegetable – three times as much as orange and about the same as blackcurrants. The iron content is exceptional and the plant is a good source of manganese and calcium. It is also very high in potassium.

In the Middle Ages parsley was used for many conditions including 'fastening teeth' (because scurvy, which is caused by a deficiency of vitamin C, makes the gums spongy and the teeth loose) and for 'brightening dim eyes' (bad eyesight is a sign of shortage of vitamin A). The old herbalists often had good results without their knowing the chemistry involved. The Ancient Greeks were in awe of parsley because the herb was associated with Archemorus who was eaten by a serpent having been put on a parsley leaf as a baby by his careless nurse. From that time on he was thought of as the harbinger of death. On the other hand, the Greeks festooned the winners of games with parsley garlands and decorated the many maidens that sang at feasts in the same way. This last custom may be associated with the great effectiveness of parsley in regularising the female menstrual cycle due to the presence of apiol, which is a constituent of the female sex hormone oestrogen. The plant was used against the effects of malaria with some success and it was said that it was one of the most proven of all remedies as a diuretic to cure water retention or dropsy.

Parsley also has the natural ability to neutralise the malodorous effects of garlic and onions. Perhaps it is an old wives' tale, but my mother used to believe that chewing parsley leaves was good for one's nerves. I also chew parsley, mainly because I like it.

Today parsley may be useful for the treatment of kidney stones, as a diuretic, for the relief of rheumatism, menstrual insufficiency and as a general stimulant. It settles the stomach and improves the appetite. The high content of vitamin C is not only useful in its own right, but also assists the absorption of the valuable quantity of iron. Parsley juice, being a herbal drink, is quite powerful. It is usually taken therapeutically in quantities of about 60 ml (2 fl oz) three times a day and is best mixed with other juices. The leaves can be frozen and are easily stored. It is a good idea to use parsley in cooking as well as in the form of juice.

PARSNIP

Parsnips look a bit like overgrown albino carrots. In olden days, before potatoes were deemed edible, the parsnip was prized not only for its long storage life, but also for its sweet, nutty taste and nutritional value. Parsnips can be eaten raw as well as cooked, a fact not many people realise.

Parsnips are often overlooked when it comes to juicing and they really shouldn't be. Make sure to make the most of this winter vegetable when it is in season. Parsnip juice is sweet (along the same lines as carrot juice), but has its own distinctive taste. By itself the sweetness of parsnip juice can be a bit much, so try mixing it with other juices such as apple, spinach and celery.

When selecting parsnips for juicing look for produce that is cream-coloured, firm to the touch and medium-sized. Avoid overly large parsnips that have been left in the ground for too long, as their fibres will be woody and bitter rather than succulent.

If your parsnips are organic, simply remove any attached soil, rinse them and remove the tops and tails. Cut the parsnips into small pieces that are suitable for feeding into your juicer. If your parsnips are not organic, you may want to peel them first as you would carrots.

The health benefits of parsnips are again underrated. Parsnip juice contains far less calories than carrot juice and so is a valuable ingredient in juice recipes that aim to help weight loss. Parsnips are a good source of folic acid, potassium, sulphur and vitamin C. This makes parsnip juice a valuable ally in the quest for healthy skin. Parsnip has been associated with improving bronchial tube function in the lungs and so may be of benefit to those who suffer from asthma.

TOMATO

Although the tomato is really a fruit in the botanical sense, it is commonly classified as a vegetable as it has a savoury rather than sweet taste. Tomato is rich in calcium, niacin, potassium, phosphorus, vitamins A, B6 and C, folate, fibre and carbohydrate.

Tomatoes were originally native to the western side of South America, including the Galapagos Islands. The first type of tomato grown is thought to have resembled the smaller-sized cherry tomato more than the larger varieties.

This fruit intrigued the Mexican Indians since it resembled the tomatillo, which was a staple in their cuisine. The Spanish Conquistadors who came to Mexico shortly after Columbus's discovery of the New World 'discovered' tomatoes and brought the seeds back to Spain, beginning the introduction of the tomato into Europe.

Although the use of tomatoes spread throughout Europe and made its way to Italy by the 16th century, it was originally not a very popular food as many people held the belief that it was poisonous since it was a member of the deadly nightshade family. They were wise, but not fully accurate – the leaves of the tomato plant, but not its fruits, do contain toxic alkaloids. Yet, due to this belief, tomatoes were more often grown as an ornamental garden plant than as a food for many more centuries in several European countries.

The tomato is now firmly entrenched in numerous cuisines (Italian, Spanish, Mexican, to name just a few) and grown in many gardens for home consumption as well as being sold commercially in its ubiquitous forms (tinned tomatoes, tomato purée, passata, juice and ketchup which was once classified as a vegetable in the United States).

A lot of recent research has shown that people who consume large amounts of tomatoes have a significantly reduced risk of developing certain types of cancers, particularly prostate cancer. While no one knows for certain why this is, the consensus seems to be that lycopene, a bioflavenoid closely related to betacarotene, is responsible. Tomatoes are even more successful in the fight against prostate and bladder cancer if they are teamed with broccoli, according to a study published in *Cancer Research*. It is also now believed that tomatoes reduce the risk of cardiovascular disease. Chinese doctors prescribe eating one or two fresh tomatoes first thing in the morning to relieve bloodshot eyes. Other health claims for tomatoes include: reducing the tendency towards blood clotting (*if* this is true, a lot of people can stop taking baby aspirin daily), cleansing skin, relieving sunburn, detoxifying the liver, improving energy and healing wounds.

And unlike most fruits and vegetables, the cooked tomato has more value in terms of lycopene than the raw tomato. Cooking also tempers the acid and bitter qualities of tomatoes and brings out their warm, rich sweetness.

Tomatoes may be juiced as a single ingredient or mixed with carrot or orange juice.

Tomatoes are also used as a viable and realistic substitute for blood in vampire films!

WATERCRESS

Delicious watercress has been grown commercially in the pure spring waters of southern England since the early 1800s.

It used to be a staple part of the working-class diet, most often eaten for breakfast in a sandwich. If the family was too poor to buy bread, they ate it by itself and so watercress became known as the 'poor man's bread'.

Street sellers bought it from the market and added their own value to the watercress by forming it into bunches. In those days, bunches were hand-held and eaten like an ice-cream cone.

The harvesting of watercress was a labour-intensive task, and in the days before rubber boots the workers wore thigh-length leather boots carefully waterproofed against the damp and hobnailed to give a grip on the base of the watercress bed.

No single food can maintain and promote good health. That comes from the overall benefits of a healthy diet and lifestyle. But some foods have been classed as 'superfoods' because they are especially rich in health-promoting nutrients, antioxidants or phytochemicals (bioactive plant compounds) and therefore pack more of a nutritional punch than others. Evidence shows that watercress is one of these.

Watercress is naturally low in calories, virtually fat free and contains a wide range of essential vitamins and minerals. It is also a source of a number of phytochemicals with potential health benefits. These include lutein, quercetin, phenolic acids and glucosinolates.

Throughout the ages, the Egyptians, Greeks, Romans, Anglo Saxons and people belonging to many other cultures touted watercress for its health-giving benefits. Victorians thought the plant was a cure for toothache, hiccups and even freckles!

During the World War I, watercress was promoted as an important health-giving home-grown food. In the 1960s the strongest demand for watercress came from the north where, whatever the family income, high tea reigned supreme. And somehow the height of 'posh Englishness' has always been thought of as watercress or cucumber sandwiches at tea time by Americans watching old British films.

Culpeper's *Herbal* says

> '*the leaves bruised, or the juice is good to
> be applied to the face, or other parts,
> troubled with freckles, pimples, spots or the
> like, at night, and washed away in the
> morning. The juice mixed with vinegar, and
> the fore part of the head bathed therewith,
> is very good for those that are dull and
> drowsy, or have the lethargy.*
>
> '*Watercress pottage is a good remedy to
> cleanse the blood in the spring, and help
> headaches, and consume the gross humours
> winter has left behind; those that would live
> in health may use it if they please. If they
> will not I cannot help it. If any fancy not
> pottage, they may eat the herb as a salad.*'

I'm sure that if Culpeper had been around today and had access to a juicer, he would certainly have made watercress into juice.

Watercress is mentioned so often as an ingredient in detox vegetable juice recipes and as a cure for a variety of ills, that it could be viewed as a staple part of a regime for those wishing to juice their way to health.

BLENDED VEGETABLE JUICE – V8

For many years V8 Vegetable Juice, a 100% blend of eight vegetables (tomatoes, carrots, celery, beets, parsley, lettuce, watercress and spinach) provided an easy way to consume healthy vegetable juices.

The company is still going strong and the American Heart Association has endorsed V8 Vegetable Juice as meeting 'food criteria for saturated fat and cholesterol for healthy people over age two'.

But if you are reading this book, you are probably more interested in making your own healthy drinks, so you might want to look at the recipe for home-made Vegetable Juice Cocktail on page 126.

GRASS JUICES

Juicing cereal grasses, particularly wheatgrass, has become a kind of health fad, with all sorts of claims as to its efficacy in healing anything that ails you.

Wheatgrass refers to the young grass of the common wheat plant (*Triticum aestivum*) that is freshly juiced or dried into powder for human and animal consumption. Both provide chlorophyll, amino acids, minerals, vitamins and enzymes. Claims about wheatgrass health benefits range from providing supplemental nutrition to having unique curative properties. Some consumers grow and juice wheatgrass in their homes. It is often available in juice bars, alone or in mixed fruit and/or vegetable drinks. It is also available in many health food stores as fresh produce, tablets, frozen juice and powder.

Some of the health claims made for wheatgrass (and some say barley grass as well) are that it is one of the best sources of living chlorophyll available. Chlorophyll is anti-bacterial and can be used inside and outside the body as a healer. Proponents of wheatgrass also say that wheatgrass juice is a superior detoxification agent compared with carrot juice and other fruits and vegetables. They maintain that wheatgrass juice acts as a detergent in the body and is a body deodorant, gargling wheatgrass juice relieves sore throats, one should drink wheatgrass juice for skin problems such as eczema or psoriasis, wheatgrass juice improves the digestion and wheatgrass juice is great for constipation and keeping the bowels open.

There are also wilder claims. A small amount of wheatgrass juice in the diet helps prevent tooth decay. Wheatgrass juice held in the mouth for five minutes will help eliminate toothaches. It pulls poisons from the gums. Wheatgrass juice keeps the hair from greying. Wheatgrass juice can remove heavy metals from the body. Wheatgrass juice is great for blood disorders of all kinds.

Wheatgrass juice may be the health tonic of the moment, but the evidence for its benefits is rather thin on the ground. In addition, too much wheatgrass consumption can cause nausea and diarrhoea.

Spirulina, a blue-green algae, became popular in the 1980s as a 'miracle' weight loss product. This idea has largely been disproved, but its qualities as a nutritional supplement entices many people to add it to juice mixtures.

Spirulina claims to offer more protein than any other food, contains all eight essential amino acids and 10 non-essential amino acids. It has a high iron, calcium and mineral content, contains essential fatty acid GLA, natural carotenes and antioxidants, a wide spectrum of vitamins and has a low fat content.

Don't use it if you have hyperparathyroidism, seafood allergies, or if you have a high fever.

In short, add these grasses to your juices by all means, but they are not a substitute for eating a variety of fruits and vegetables.

FRUIT JUICE
RECIPES

FRUIT JUICE RECIPES

All of these recipes assume you will be using a centrifugal or masticating juicer, except for citrus juice, which can just be squeezed. They also start with fresh fruit, unless they say otherwise. Fruit should be ripe but not overripe. While all fruit and vegetables should be washed before juicing, you should avoid soaking them to preserve the nutrients.

It is not necessary to peel most fruit, but if you choose to do so, take off the thinnest layer possible.

Ideally you should only process as much juice as you will be drinking at one time. To avoid oxidation you can add a squeeze of lemon juice.

If there are no specific instructions listed in a recipe, simply put the ingredients into a juicer and process until smooth.

These recipes are only meant to provide a starting point. Be creative and experiment with any fruits and vegetables you fancy.

LIST OF RECIPES

APPLE JUICE IDEAS

Home-made apple juice is delicious, but only make as much as you can drink because it will not keep.

APPLE-GINGER ZINGER

Serves 2

> 3 dessert apples of your choice (e.g. Cox, Granny Smith, Worcester Pearmain), pared if desired and cored
>
> 2.5 cm (1 inch) piece of fresh ginger, peeled

APPLE-CARROT

Serves 2

> 3 dessert apples of your choice, pared if desired and cored
>
> 2 carrots, scraped

PEAR-APPLE ORCHARD

Serves 2

> 3 dessert apples of your choice, pared if desired and cored
>
> 1 ripe Conference or Comice pear, cored

BLUSHING EVE

Serves 2

> 3 dessert apples of your choice, pared if desired and cored
>
> 1 ripe peach, stone removed
>
> 8 large fresh strawberries, hulled

APPLE-CURRANT

Serves 4
>3 dessert apples of your choice, pared if desired and cored
>225 g (8 oz) fresh blackcurrants

APPLE BLUES

Serves 4
>3 dessert apples of your choice, pared if desired and cored
>225 g (8 oz) fresh blueberries

APPLEBERRY

Serves 4
>3 dessert apples of your choice, pared if desired and cored
>115 g (4 oz) fresh raspberries
>115 g (4 oz) fresh blackberries

APPLE CITRUS COOLER

Serves 4
>3 dessert apples of your choice, pared if desired and cored
>1 grapefruit
>1 mandarin orange

CRANAPPLE

Serves 2
>2 dessert apples of your choice, pared if desired and cored
>115 g (4 oz) fresh or frozen cranberries

BERRY BLENDS

RAZZLE DAZZLE

This drink has a wonderful creamy goodness

Serves 2-4
  225 g (8 oz) fresh raspberries
  $1/2$ cantaloupe melon, rind and seeds removed
  1 stick celery

BLUSHING PEACH

Serves 2
  115 g (4 oz) fresh strawberries
  2 fresh ripe peaches, stoned

STRAWBERRY PINEAPPLE JOY

Serves 4
  115 g (4 oz) fresh strawberries
  225 g (8 oz) fresh pineapple, skinned and chunked
  2 large oranges

BUG JUICE

You will need   Serves 4

    450 g (1 lb) strawberries

    2 lemons

    600 ml (1 pint) ginger beer

    85 g (3 oz) dried cranberries

    85 g (3 oz) fresh blueberries

Put all ingredients into a juicer and process until smooth. If too tart, add a little sugar.

CITRUS JUICE IDEAS

GRAPEFRUIT JUICE

My very favourite! I prefer the sharpness of white grapefruit juice, but you could try mixing white and pink or white and red or even pink and red and see which one you prefer. One grapefruit should yield about 180 ml (6 fl oz) juice

THE COLD CHASER

Serves 2

    1 grapefruit, any colour

    1 dessert apple of your choice, pared if desired
        and cored

    2 carrots, scraped

    1 cm ($1/2$ in) fresh ginger root

BLUEBERRY HILL

Serves 2

> 1 grapefruit, any colour
> 1 handful fresh or frozen blueberries

GRAPEFRUIT SUNSET

Serves 2

> 1 pink grapefruit
> 60 g (2 oz) fresh strawberries
> 60 g (2 oz) fresh raspberries
> $1/2$ lemon

ONLY JUST

The favourite juice of the Western world. And if you think freshly-squeezed juice from cartons is delicious, just wait until you squeeze your own. Make sure you have oranges that look juicy for the best results.

Allow 2 large oranges for each person These should yield about 150–180 ml (5–6 fl oz) juice.

DOCTOR PEPPER

Serves 2

> 4 oranges
> $1/2$ red pepper
> 1 stick celery

ST CLEMENS

Serves 2
   4 oranges
   1 lemon
   Squeeze of lime

BLACK ARTS

Serves 2
   1 white grapefruit
   115 g (4 oz) fresh blackberries

UNDERCURRANT

Serves 2
   4 oranges
   115 g (4 oz) blackcurrants

CITRUS SLURP

Citrus juice made with a hand citrus juicer and juice made with a centrifugal juice extractor can be quite different. The juice extractor produces a thick frothy juice, which is more tart. The quality and the nutritional value of the two are similar so it is only a matter of preference. This is an awesome wake-up call. It takes a little time to make, but it is worth it because you will find yourself feeling much sharper for the rest of the day.

Serves 2
   2 grapefruit
   2 oranges

COUGHBUSTER

A citrus drink with the added bonus of garlic and onion, which acts as a natural expectorant.

Serves 1

> 1 small garlic clove
> 1/4 mild red onion
> 1/2 lemon
> 1 orange
> 5 ml (1 tsp) honey (preferably Manuka)

1. Put the garlic, onion, lemon and orange into a juice extractor and process.
2. Pour into a mug and whisk in the honey.

FIVE ALIVE

Serves 2

> 1 grapefruit
> 1 orange
> 1 satsuma
> 1 mandarin orange
> 1 lime

BLOODY MIMOSA

Serves 2

> 4 blood oranges
> 2 ripe peaches, stoned

BLUE ORANGE

Serves 2

> 115 g (4 oz) blueberries
> 2 oranges

HOME-MADE CRANBERRY JUICE

Much better than store-bought!

Makes about 1 litre (2 pints)
  450 g (1 lb) fresh or frozen cranberries
  1 litre (1¾ pints) water
  2–3 orange slices
  Pinch of salt
  115 g (4 oz) caster sugar

1. Wash the fresh cranberries and put into a saucepan with the water, orange slices and salt. Bring to the boil and cook until the cranberries pop, 10–15 minutes.
2. Remove from the heat and turn the cranberry mixture into a muslin-lined sieve.
3. Strain without pressing the berries and reserve the pulp to make cranberry sauce.
4. Return the juice to the saucepan, add the sugar and boil for 2–3 minutes. Taste and add more sugar if needed.
5. Cool the juice and chill before serving.

DEVIL JUICE

Serves 1
  90 ml (3 fl oz) cranberry juice
  90 ml (3 fl oz) tomato juice
  5 ml (1 tsp) Tabasco sauce
  5 ml (1 tsp) lemon juice
  Pinch of freshly ground black pepper
  Pinch of salt
  Lemon twists and parsley to garnish

Combine ingredients in a jug and pour into an ice-filled glass.

FRUIT NECTAR

The raspberries add a little colour and substance to this drink and you don't even have to sieve them unless you are an absolute purist, suffer from diverticular disease or any other health problem that would keep you from eating seeds.

Makes 1 serving

60 g (2 oz) raspberries, fresh or thawed from frozen

1 orange, peeled and sectioned

1 nectarine, pitted and sliced

HOME-MADE GRAPE JUICE

Equipment:

A colander for rinsing the grapes

1 large, 12-litre/21-pint pan

1 6- or 8-litre /10½–14-pint pan

A very large fine mesh sieve, or muslin

1. Pick the grapes. Get a large basket, wear long sleeves and a hat, bring clippers, and fill up the basket with grape bunches. Keep in mind that 450 g (1 lb) grapes will yield a little less than 240 ml (8 fl oz) of juice. If you are making juice from purchased grapes, you can eliminate this step.

2. Wash and stem the grapes. Put grapes in a basin filled with water. Then rinse the individual grapes, picking them away from the stem, collecting the grapes in a large bowl, and discarding the green, unripe and old shrivelled grapes.

3. Mash the grapes. With a potato masher, mash away at the grapes so the juice begins to flow. If you have picked a lot of grapes, you may need to work in

batches. You can probably mash about 1.8 kg (4 lb) grapes at a time.

4. Cook the grapes. Put the mashed grapes into a large stockpot. Slowly heat the grapes and juice to a simmer on a medium heat and then simmer for 10 minutes. Stir occasionally so that the grapes don't stick to the bottom of the pan. Halfway through cooking, mash the grapes again, breaking up as many of the remaining grapes as possible.

5. Prepare sieve or muslin. Get another large pan; place a large fine mesh sieve over it. Alternatively, you can cover it with two layers of muslin, secured with an elastic band. Make sure that the pan is sitting on a plate to catch any juice that may run over.

6. Strain grape mixture. Ladle grape mixture over sieve or muslin to strain. Let sit for several hours or overnight in the refrigerator to strain completely.

7. Finishing. Remove sieve or muslin. Note that sediment will have formed on the bottom of the container. Rinse out the sieve or muslin and strain the juice again, to filter out some of the sediment. Pour or ladle juice into containers.

ORANGE, APRICOT AND GINGER

Fruity and gingery, this juice is high in vitamin C and betacarotene

Serves 2

280 g (10 oz) fresh apricots, stoned

4 large oranges, peeled

2.5 cm (1 in) piece fresh ginger

2.5 ml (½ tsp) sunflower seeds

Put all ingredients into a blender and whiz until smooth.

PEAR-APPLE BEET

This rosy drink counts as one of your five-a-day

Serves 2

2 ripe pears

2 dessert apples of your choice

1 beetroot

FRESH PINEAPPLE JUICE

The juice yield will depend upon the size of the pineapple, but it should produce 30% juice based on its weight.

1 large pineapple

Water as needed

1. Remove rind of pineapple and discard. Cut pineapple into chunks.

2. Put the pineapple into a large saucepan with enough water to barely cover it. Bring to the boil and boil rapidly for 10 minutes. Remove from the heat.
3. Strain the juice through a muslin-covered sieve.
4. Pour the juice into clean sterilised jars and screw on the lids. Process in a boiling water bath for 10 minutes.

STRAWBERRY JUICE

This produces a wonderfully pure juice that will keep in the fridge for several days and has many other uses, from pouring over ice cream to the base for a cordial. (The method works equally well with raspberries.) These quantities will make about 240 ml (8 fl oz) of juice, though it can be reduced to taste. The fructose intensifies the strawberry flavour, but this will still be delicious made with sugar instead.

750 g (1¾ lb) strawberries, washed and hulled
70 g (2½ oz) fructose (or icing or caster sugar)

1. Quarter the strawberries and place in a bowl. Sprinkle with the fructose (or sugar) and cover with clingfilm. Choose a saucepan over which the bowl will sit snugly, fill with 3–4 cm (¾ in) water and place over a very low heat. Place the covered bowl on top of the pan and leave for an hour and a half; the water should be only lightly simmering. Take care not to let it evaporate and top up as necessary.
2. When the time is up, carefully lift the bowl from the pan and remove the clingfilm. Place clean, unused double muslin or dry J-cloth in another bowl, so that it lines the bowl and hangs over the edges.

Tip the still-warm contents of the strawberry bowl into the cloth-lined bowl. Gather together the edges of the cloth, thereby enclosing the mix; you should now have a bag-shaped package. Using string, tie shut the neck of the bag and then hang the sack from a shelf of the fridge. Place a bowl underneath to catch the juices, and leave to drain overnight. Next day, discard the contents of the sack – all of the strawberry flavour will have been taken out of the fruit, so there won't be much to be gained from eating it.

SUN JUICE

Serves 2

    4 medium oranges

    Wedge of very ripe papaya

    1 large overripe banana

    1 cm ($\frac{1}{2}$ inch) fresh ginger root

    Crushed ice

Put all of the ingredients into a blender and process until smooth.

WATERMELON JUICE

Serves 4

    675 g (1$\frac{1}{2}$ lb) watermelon pulp, seeded,
        cut into chunks

    30 g (1 oz) sugar

    Juice of 1 lime

    1 handful ice cubes

Put all of the ingredients into a blender and blend until smooth.

FRUIT JUICE DRINK RECIPES

FRESH LEMONADE OR LIMEADE

Ingredients
- 450 g (1 lb) sugar or 55 g (2 oz) granulated sugar substitute
- 240 ml (8 fl oz) filtered water
- 240 ml (8 fl oz) freshly squeezed lemon or lime juice
- Water and ice to make 2 litres (3½ pints)

1. Make a syrup with the sugar and the 240 ml (8 fl oz) of the filtered water. Stir to dissolve the sugar.
2. Add the freshly squeezed juice. Stir.
3. Add water and ice to make 2 litres (3½ pints). Serve ice cold.

HONEYDEW JUICE DRINK

Serves 6
- 1.8 kg (4 lb) ripe honeydew melon
- About 480 ml (16 fl oz) measure ice cubes
- 240 ml (8 fl oz) filtered water
- 30 g (1 oz) sugar or to taste
- Lemon juice (optional)

1. Cut melon into wedges and remove and discard the seeds and rind. Cut melon into 2.5 cm (1 in) pieces.
2. In a blender combine half the melon with half the ice cubes, water, sugar and lemon juice, if using. Blend until very smooth. Pour the juice into a pitcher and repeat with the remaining ingredients.

KIWI GATORADE

Serves 4

4 kiwi fruits, peeled

55 g (2 oz) caster sugar

Juice from 3 limes (about 120 ml/4 fl oz)

300 ml (10 fl oz) unsweetened pineapple juice

450 ml (15 fl oz) sparkling or still mineral water

Crushed ice

Place all of the ingredients into a blender with crushed ice and process for 1 minute.

LIMORANGE

Makes about 3 pints (1.8 litres)

225 g (8 oz) sugar

240 ml (8 fl oz) water

5 ml (1 tsp) grated lemon rind

5 ml (1 tsp) grated orange rind

750 ml (1¼ pints) filtered ice water

16 fl oz (480 ml) freshly squeezed orange juice

60 ml (2 fl oz) freshly squeezed lemon juice

1. Make a simple syrup. In a saucepan, combine the sugar, 240 ml (8 fl oz) water, lemon rind and orange rind. Bring to the gentle boil and cook for 8-10 minutes until thickened. Remove from the heat.
2. Pour the contents of the saucepan into a container, removing and discarding the rind. Set aside to cool to room temperature.
3. Transfer the mixture to a large jug. Stir in the ice water, orange juice and lemon juice.
4. Chill in the refrigerator or serve over ice.

NEW-FASHIONED PINK LEMONADE

This lemonade, with a gentle addition of cranberry juice, is the perfect refreshing cooler for a hot summer day.

Makes about 1.8 litres (3 pints) **Serves 6**

    280 g (10 oz) sugar (if using unsweetened cranberry
       juice, 225 g (8 oz) if using sweetened)
    1 litre (1¾ pints) filtered water
    240 ml (8 fl oz) cranberry juice
    240 ml (8 fl oz) lemon juice

1. Make a simple syrup by heating the sugar and 240 ml (8 fl oz) of the water in a small saucepan until the sugar is completely dissolved. Remove from the heat.
2. Stir together the remaining water, cranberry juice, lemon juice and simple syrup. Adjust ingredients to your taste. Chill for an hour, or add ice to cool.

VEGETABLE
JUICE
RECIPES

VEGETABLE JUICE RECIPES

CARROT BLENDS

All of these carrot-based juices serve 2

RED LION

5 carrots, scraped
1 dessert apple
$1/4$ beetroot with greens

SWEET BEET

4 carrots, scraped
1 dessert apple
$1/2$ beetroot with greens
1 handful parsley

SATIN SKIN

This combination contributes to smooth satiny skin.
It's also good for colds and nausea.

4–5 carrots, scraped
1 dessert apple
1 cm ($1/2$ in) ginger root

STOMACH SOOTHER

5 carrots, scraped
7.5 cm (3 in) wedge of green cabbage
$1/2$ dessert apple

CARROT COCKTAIL

4 carrots, scraped

2 sticks celery

1 Granny Smith apple

2 fresh sorrel leaves

CARROT, TOMATO AND CUCUMBER BOOSTER

A sweet and tasty pick-me-up with betacarotene and vitamin C.

Serves 1

1 large carrot, scraped

1 large vine tomato

$1/4$ cucumber, unpared

6 basil leaves

CELERY BLENDS

ROSEMARY'S CELERY CUKE TONIC

This green juice is packed with vitamin C.

Serves 2

2.5 cm (1 in) piece fresh ginger root

2 celery sticks with leaves

1 cucumber

5 ml (1 tsp) fresh rosemary

Put all the ingredients into a juice extractor and blend until smooth.

ENERGY JUICE DRINK

Serves 2
- 6 carrots, scraped
- 4 sticks celery with leaves
- 2.5 cm (1 in) ginger root
- 1 dash chilli sauce
- 1/4 lemon

1. Juice the carrots, celery and ginger and pour into a jug.
2. Place in the refrigerator to chill.
3. When ready to serve, pour into a glass and add a dash of chilli sauce and a squeeze of lemon juice.

GREEN GARDEN

A bright green juice, bursting with vitamins.

Serves 2
- 12 young spinach leaves
- 2 green peppers, seeded
- 2 celery sticks with leaves
- 4 lettuce leaves

SPINACH JUICES

While spinach is a wonderful vegetable, full of iron and vitamins, Popeye's favourite veg can cause diarrhoea if eaten in excess. When preparing blended juices, one rule of thumb is to use only one-quarter green juice. Some of these may not look very appetising after they become juice, but they are really tasty and good for you.

Some ideas for utilising spinach are:

7-CARROT AND SPINACH

Makes about 240 ml (8 fl oz)
   7 carrots, scraped
   Handful of baby spinach leaves

1. Cut the carrots into 5–7.5 cm (2–3 in) pieces.
2. Starting and finishing with the carrots, process the carrots and spinach in a juice extractor.

SPINACH ORANGE JUICE

This mixture is quite delicious and works wonders on the complexion as it is rich in iron and vitamin C, which are needed for a clear complexion.

Serves 4
   100 g (3½ oz) baby spinach
   30 g (1 oz) fresh parsley
   Juice from 8 oranges

Put all the ingredients into a blender and whizz, then sieve, pressing down on all the solids to extract the juice.

BLUSHING POPEYE

Serves 4
   450 g (1 lb) carrots, scraped
   1 large beetroot
   Handful of baby spinach

This mixture, which needs a juice extractor, is a lovely way to get some Popeye muscle.

FRESH TOMATO JUICE

This wholesome juice is lighter in colour than commercial juice, but bursting with goodness.

Serves 2

  2 large very ripe tomatoes
  Salt and freshly ground black pepper (optional)
  Sugar and lemon juice to taste (optional)

1. Skin the tomatoes by placing them in a bowl and pouring boiling water over. Leave for 30 seconds. Plunge tomatoes into a bowl of cold water and leave for 1 minute.
2. Place a sieve over a clean bowl. Cut the tomatoes open over the sieve and squeeze the tomatoes to extract the juice.
3. Discard the seeds. Place the tomato pulp and juice into a blender and process. Taste the juice and add salt, pepper, sugar and lemon juice to taste.
4. Serve immediately or chill in the refrigerator.

VEGEMATO JUICE

Makes about 1½ litres (2¼ pints)

  2.25 kg (4.5 lbs)ripe tomatoes
  1 carrot, chopped
  1 stick celery with leaves, chopped
  ½ green pepper, seeded and chopped
  30 ml (2 tbsp) chopped onion
  Fresh lemon juice

1. Remove core and blossom ends of tomatoes and cut into quarters. Tip into a preserving pan or stockpot.

2. Add the carrot, celery, green pepper and onion, bring to the boil and simmer for 20 minutes, until all the vegetables are soft.

3. Remove from the heat and press through a fine sieve into a large bowl or jug.

4. Measure the juice and add 15 ml (1 tbsp) lemon juice to each 450 ml (15 fl oz) vegetable juice.

This mixture will keep for about 1 week, covered in the refrigerator. Alternatively, pour into sterilised jars and process.

HOME-MADE V8 JUICE

If you grow tomatoes and have a glut, you might consider making your own juice and bottling it. Alternatively, you can freeze it if you have enough freezer space.

Makes about 5.5 litres (about 9½ pints)
>   6.75 kg (15 lb) ripe tomatoes
>   1 bunch celery with leaves, chopped
>   3 large mild onions, chopped
>   3 garlic cloves, mashed
>   10 ml (2 tsp) salt
>   4 ml ($3/4$ tsp) freshly ground black pepper
>   10 ml (2 tsp) prepared horseradish
>   75 ml (5 tbsp) lemon juice
>   Worcestershire sauce to taste
>   55 g (2 oz) caster sugar

1. Remove core and blossom ends of tomatoes and cut into quarters. Tip into a large preserving pan or stockpot.

2. Add the tomatoes, celery, onions and garlic, bring to the boil and simmer for about 20 minutes. Remove from the heat.

3. In a blender or food processor, process in batches until smooth. Strain and discard the pulp.

4. Return to the preserving pan: add the salt, pepper, horseradish, lemon juice, Worcestershire sauce and sugar. Bring to the boil, and then remove from the heat. If you are freezing it, cool, and then freeze in suitable containers.

5. If you are bottling the juice, pour the hot juice carefully into glass jars, which have been washed, dried and sterilised (heat in a moderate oven for 5 minutes, or in a microwave oven for 1 minute), and seal while still hot. Ensure that the centre of the lid is sucked down once the jars are cool.

SMOOTHIE
RECIPES

SMOOTHIES

A smoothie is a blended, chilled, usually sweet beverage made from fresh fruit (or sometimes vegetables). In addition to fruit, many smoothies include chilled or frozen yoghurt, non-dairy milk, tea, seeds and nuts, grains and crushed ice.

They have a milkshake-like consistency, but unlike milkshakes, they do not usually contain cow's milk or ice cream. Smoothies are marketed to health-conscious people, and some juice bars and cafes offer smoothies made with soya milk, green tea, herbal supplements or nutritional supplements. If it can be drunk from a glass or sipped from a straw, but so thick you could eat it with a spoon, it is a smoothie.

If it had not been for the advent of the blender, the smoothie wouldn't exist. The blender was invented in 1922 by Stephen Poplawski to make malteds and milkshakes at American soda fountains and ice cream parlours. It was the first time anyone had ever put a spinning blade at the bottom of a container with an electrical base. It was refined and improved by Fred Osius in 1935, who apparently ran into financial trouble and approached a bandleader, Fred Waring, to back the machine. This he did, but soon booted Mr Osius out of the company and renamed it Waring. The rest is history – the Waring Blender was one of the great inventions of the 20th century. It was on the top of every bride's wedding register list around 1960.

California health food shops were already selling thick puréed fruit drinks as early as the 1950s. The leap from milkshake to smoothie occurred in the USA in the early 1960s when the word was coined in a blender cookery book. Smoothies became popular on several levels: they were a much more portable breakfast than a bowl of cereal and milk and they had the benefit of being deemed healthy. By the 1990s and 2000s, smoothies had become available at mainstream cafés and coffee shops and in pre-bottled versions at supermarkets.

A smoothie consists of three different ingredient consistencies: solid, liquid and binder. The solid is the puréed fruits or vegetables, the liquid is the milk, tea, fruit juice, etc. and the binder or emulsifier is the ingredient that makes the smoothie thick and creamy, such as yoghurt, tofu or bananas.

When you are making a smoothie there are very few rules to follow. Smoothies are usually enjoyed chilled, so some, but certainly not all, of the ingredients should be frozen. The more frozen ingredients you add, the thicker your smoothie will be. One ingredient should always be liquid or a smooth and creamy solid like yoghurt.

Smoothies are really more about pleasure than juices. Yes, you get the benefits of fruit and vegetables and yes, if you make them yourself you know exactly what you have put into them, but it is probably a given that they will contain more calories than the same quantity of juice.

However, having a smoothie filled with healthy ingredients for dessert or as a snack is much better for you than having a hot fudge sundae or a piece of cake, and it could be just as enjoyable.

LIST OF RECIPES

SMOOTHIE RECIPES

ALMOND FRUIT SMOOTHIE

Whoever said healthy smoothies don't have to taste good never tasted this gorgeous recipe.

Serves 2

  240 ml (8 fl oz) fresh orange juice

  115 g (4 oz) frozen peaches

  1 frozen banana, cut into chunks

  30 ml (2 tbsp) toasted flaked almonds

Put all the ingredients into a blender and process until smooth.

N.B. To toast almonds, spread them on an ungreased baking sheet. Preheat the oven to 180°C (350°F/Gas Mark 4). Toast for 5–10 minutes, until light brown. Stir once or twice to ensure even browning.

APPLE AND APRICOT SMOOTHIE

Serves 2–4

  1 dessert apple, peeled, cored and chopped

  240 ml (8 fl oz) apple juice

  4 fresh apricots, stoned

  1 banana, peeled

  175 g (6 oz) plain yoghurt

  15 ml (1 tbsp) runny honey

  10 ice cubes

Put all the ingredients into a blender and purée until smooth.

APPLE BARLEY SMOOTHIE

If you are constipated or have skin problems such as acne, a fibre-rich smoothie will help you to achieve both smooth skin and bowel regularity.

Serves 2

> 1 medium apple, unpeeled
> 30 g (2 oz) barley, cooked
> 60 ml (4 tbsp) raisins
> 1.25 ml (¼ tsp) vanilla essence
> 5 ml (1 tsp) runny honey
> 360 ml (12 fl oz) rice milk
> 5 ml (1 tsp) lecithin granules*
> 30 ml (2 tbsp) flaxseed oil

1. Add all the ingredients to a blender and process, ensuring that you add the lecithin.
2. Chill in the fridge and serve cold.

*Lecithin helps to break down the flaxseed oil into tiny droplets and makes it more digestible.

APPLE, BANANA, CARROT, ORANGE AND DATE SMOOTHIE

Using equal quantities of apple, banana, carrot and orange produces a glorious smoothie. The addition of dates provides extra healthy sweetness.

Serves 2

1 dessert apple, peeled, cored and chopped
1 large ripe banana, peeled
1 large carrot, scraped and chunked
1 large orange, peeled, seeds removed
3 dates, stoned
45 ml (3 tbsp) flaxseed (optional)
10 ice cubes

Place the ingredients in a blender and process until smooth. If the mixture is too thick, add a little filtered water and process again.

BANANA-COFFEE SMOOTHIE

This perfectly smooth, perfectly delicious smoothie is a wonderful way to start the day. The milk and yoghurt should be very cold before blending.

Serves 2

2 small or 1 large banana, peeled, cut up and frozen
360 ml (12 fl oz) oat milk
200 g (7 oz) low-fat coffee yoghurt
1.25 ml ($^1/_4$ tsp) ground cinnamon
Ground nutmeg, to serve

1. Combine the frozen bananas, oat milk, yoghurt and cinnamon in a blender container.
2. Cover and whizz until smooth.

3. To serve, pour into glasses and dust with a sprinkle of ground nutmeg.

BANANA COLADA

This is a great way to use up bananas that are too ripe to eat! Just slice and put them in a plastic freezer bag and they will be there when you need them.

Serves 2
120 ml (4 fl oz) tinned coconut milk
30 ml (2 tbsp) lime juice
4 medium-sized very ripe bananas, sliced and frozen
75 ml (5 tbsp) coconut flakes or desiccated coconut

1. Add some of the coconut milk and the lime juice to a blender. With the blender running, add the bananas through the food tube.
2. Stop the blender and scrape the ingredients down. Add the remainder of the coconut milk and scrape down the mixture if needed. Blend only until smooth.
3. Add the coconut and blend for another 5 seconds.
4. Serve immediately.

BERRY NICE SMOOTHIE

You don't need to add ice if you are using frozen berries.

Serves 2
120 ml (4 fl oz) vanilla soya milk
120 ml (4 fl oz) fresh orange juice
30 g (1 oz) wheat germ
500 g (18 oz) frozen mixed berries

Put all the singredients into a blender and process until smooth.

BERRY LEMON YOGHURT SMOOTHIE

90 g (3 oz) blackberries
90 g (3 oz) blueberries
90 g (3 oz) raspberries
90 g (3 oz) strawberries
60 g (2 oz) caster sugar
2 whole unwaxed lemons
350 g (12 oz) low-fat vanilla or lemon yoghurt

Put all the ingredients into a blender and process until smooth.

BETTER THAN BREAKFAST SMOOTHIE

Everyone knows that breakfast is the most important meal of the day and skipping it is not a good idea, but trying to get your children ready for school, or you and your partner ready for work in addition to eating a good breakfast sometimes seems impossible.

Here's an idea – take your juice, cereal, fruit and yoghurt and whizz them all up together for an unbeatable meal any time of the day.

Serves 2

60 g (2 oz) granola cereal
115 g (4 oz) low-fat vanilla yoghurt
10 ice cubes, crushed
1 banana
2 cups fresh juice of your choice
(e.g. apple, orange, pineapple)

1. Put all the ingredients in a blender and blend on high speed until smooth and thick.

2. Tip the contents into two thermos flasks and go on your way.

BLACKBERRY BANANA SMOOTHIE

Britain's favourite wild berry is used here to delicious advantage.

Serves 4

    500 g (18 oz) low-fat vanilla yoghurt
    1 frozen banana, cut into chunks
    250 g (9 oz) fresh or frozen blackberries

Put all the ingredients into a blender and process until smooth. If the mixture is too thick, blend in some low-fat milk.

BLUEBERRY BREEZE

I prefer frozen blueberries instead of fresh ones in this recipe because the colour is brighter and the texture is smoother.

Serves 3–4

    250 g (9 oz) frozen blueberries
    200 ml (7 fl oz) vanilla yoghurt
    360 ml (12 fl oz) low-fat milk

Process all the ingredients in a blender until smooth, stopping to scrape down the sides. Serve immediately.

BLUEBERRY-PINEAPPLE SMOOTHIE

A creamy combination of blueberries, banana, honey and pineapple.

Serves 4

- 250 g (9 oz) blueberries
- 2 ripe medium bananas, peeled
- 250 g (9 oz) fresh pineapple
- 200 g (7 oz) natural yoghurt
- 30 ml (2 tbsp) runny honey

Put all the ingredients into a blender and process until smooth.

CHEERY CHERRY SMOOTHIE

Fresh cherries, cherry yoghurt and just a hint of vanilla make a very delectable rosy red drink.

Serves 2

- 240 ml (8 fl oz) milk
- 1 very ripe banana
- 200 g (7 oz) low-fat cherry yoghurt
- 340 g (12 oz) fresh cherries, stoned
- 1.25 ml (1/4 tsp) vanilla extract

1. Blend the milk with the banana and yoghurt on high for 1 minute.
2. Add the cherries and vanilla extract and blend on low speed for 30 seconds.
3. Refrigerate until cold, then froth up again in the blender for a few seconds.
4. Enjoy!

COCOABANANA PEANUT BUTTER SMOOTHIE

This ticks all the boxes for those who like bananas, peanut butter and chocolate. If you have it for breakfast, it will energise you until lunchtime.

Serves 2

480 ml (16 fl oz) almond milk

2 tbsp unsweetened cocoa powder

1 banana, peeled and frozen

30 ml (2 tbsp) creamy peanut butter

Put all the ingredients into a blender container and process until smooth.

COCONUT MILK SMOOTHIE

A very subtle tropical taste.

Serves 4

300 g (11 oz) frozen blueberries

3 ripe bananas

200 g (7 oz) low-fat yoghurt

240 ml (8 fl oz) unsweetened coconut milk

30 ml (2 tbsp) runny honey

Put all the ingredients in a blender and process until smooth. Serve cold.

CRANAPPLE-LIME SMOOTHIE

Serves 2 generously
>   240 ml (8 fl oz) cranberry juice
>   240 ml (8 fl oz) apple juice
>   360 ml (12 fl oz) lime juice
>   2 scoops lime sorbet
>   75 g (3 oz) caster sugar, or to taste
>   5 ice cubes, crushed

Put all the ingredients into a blender and process until smooth.

CRANBERRY-ORANGE SMOOTHIE

Serves 3–4
>   120 ml (4 fl oz) cranberry juice
>   60 ml (4 tbsp) cranberry sauce
>   2 large oranges, peeled, pith removed and chopped
>   115 g (4 oz) orange sorbet
>   4 ice cubes made from orange juice

1. Combine cranberry juice, cranberry sauce and oranges in a blender. Blend on high speed until oranges are puréed and mixture is smooth.
2. Add the sorbet and ice cubes and blend again until mixture is smooth. Serve immediately.

N.B. Ice cubes can be made from any flavour of fruit juice and, once frozen, can be stored in zip-lock bags in the freezer.

CREAMY FRUIT BOWL SMOOTHIE

The surprise ingredient in this smoothie is an avocado, which adds a creamy richness. It will be very popular, even for people who don't normally like avocados.

Serves 4

2 very ripe bananas
480 ml (16 fl oz) fresh orange juice
115 g (4 oz) fresh strawberries
240 ml (8 fl oz) strawberry sorbet
1 ripe avocado, peeled and stoned
5 ice cubes, crushed

Put all the ingredients into a blender and process until smooth.

DREAMY CREAMY PRUNE SMOOTHIE

Makes 3–4 servings

225 g (8 oz) low-fat vanilla yoghurt
120 ml (4 fl oz) semi-skimmed milk
115 g (4 oz) soft stoned prunes
1 purple plum, stone removed and sliced
4 ice cubes

1. Combine the yoghurt, milk, prunes and plum in a blender. Blend on high speed until fruit is puréed and mixture is smooth.
2. Add ice cubes and blend again until smooth. Serve immediately.

FIVE FRUITS SMOOTHIE

A pretty good start for your five-a-day. I mix cranberry juice into the breakfast orange juice or grapefruit juice all the time and it tastes terrific.

Serves 2

2 frozen bananas, chunked

1 handful fresh blueberries

6 fresh strawberries

240 ml (8 fl oz) cranberry juice

120 ml (4 fl oz) fresh orange or grapefruit juice

Put all the ingredients into a blender and blend until smooth.

FRUIT AND MINT SMOOTHIE

This thick, frosty recipe is reminiscent of a Mojito.

45 g ($1\frac{1}{2}$ oz) red seedless grapes, frozen

60 ml (4 tbsp) unsweetened apple sauce

15 ml (1 tbsp) fresh lime juice

3 large frozen strawberries

175 g (6 oz) fresh pineapple, cubed

3 fresh mint leaves

Put the frozen grapes, applesauce and lime juice into a blender and process until smooth. Add the frozen strawberries, pineapple and mint leaves and process again until almost smooth.

GILBERT GRAPE SMOOTHIE

Serves 2–3

500 ml (16 fl oz) container vanilla soya-based ice cream
240 ml (8 fl oz) purple grape juice
240 ml (8 fl oz) vanilla or plain soya milk
5 ice cubes, crushed

Put all the ingredients into a blender and process until smooth.

GRANOLA GRAPE SMOOTHIE

Breakfast in a glass!

Serves 3–4

180 ml (6 fl oz) vanilla or plain soya milk
1.25 ml ($1/4$ tsp) ground cinnamon
400 g (14 oz) seedless red grapes
85 g (3 oz) raisins, plumped up with boiling water, then drained and cooled
60 ml (4 tbsp) granola cereal
120 ml (4 fl oz) vanilla soya-based ice cream

1. Combine the soya milk, cinnamon, grapes and raisins in a blender and blend on high speed until the fruit is puréed and the mixture is smooth.
2. Add the granola and blend again until granola is evenly distributed.
3. Add the vanilla soya ice cream and blend again until mixture is smooth. Serve immediately.

GREEN GODDESS SMOOTHIE

This combination of ingredients may sound a little strange but, believe me, it works and the avocado provides an extra layer of creaminess, even for people who don't like avocados.

Serves 4

> 2 very ripe bananas
> 480 ml (16 fl oz) freshly squeezed orange juice
> 115 g (4 oz) fresh or frozen strawberries
> 250 g (9 oz) strawberry sorbet
> 5 ice cubes, crushed
> 1 very ripe avocado, peeled and stoned

1. Put all the ingredients in a blender container and process until smooth.
2. Serve immediately.

GREEN TEA SMOOTHIES

A green tea smoothie is especially full of antioxidants for health and for boosting your immune system. If you don't have time for breakfast, make your smoothie the evening before and take it along with you to school or work. Here's a simple, vitamin-filled green tea smoothie recipe, which allows you to add the health benefits of green tea to your daily diet.

Begin with 500 ml (16 fl oz) green tea, made with 4 green tea bags, which will make it nice and strong.

Pour the green tea into a blender and add any or all of the following:

1 banana, source of potassium for your heart, cells and
   muscles, and fibre for digestive health
115 g (4 oz) live yoghurt, any flavour, a great source of
   probiotics for digestive health
1 handful blueberries or strawberries to boost your
   immune system
1 tablespoon of whey protein, providing leucine, which
   spurs weight loss
a dash of ground cinnamon to reduce your cholesterol
   and regulate your blood sugar
crushed ice to make your smoothie cold and thick

This healthy green tea smoothie is packed with
antioxidants, protein, vitamins and minerals and
makes a quick meal. If you'd like to add some fibre,
throw in a couple of tablespoons of porridge oats.

Blend until all ingredients are smooth. You don't have
to limit yourself to these ingredients. Other possible
additions are orange juice, mango, kiwi fruit, or
berries, honey, peanut butter and cherry juice.

You can also try flavoured green teas for variety.

GUAVA-MANGO FIESTA

This is a Latin American take on a smoothie and it is
full of tropical goodness.

Serves 3–4
1 ripe guava, peeled, seeded and chopped
1 ripe mango, peeled, stoned and chopped
400 g (14 oz) low-fat vanilla yoghurt
Juice of 1/2 lime
Honey, to taste
Juice or milk, if needed

1. Put all the ingredients except honey into a blender and whizz until smooth.
2. Taste and add honey to sweeten.
3. Sieve, if you like, but this will have more fibre if just blended.
4. If it is too thick for your taste, add a bit of juice or milk.

LEMONADE LIFT

Classic still lemonade, such a refresher in the summer, is used here to make a lovely tart smoothie with a pink blush.

Serves 2

240 ml (8 fl oz) home-made or bought good quality still lemonade
60 g (2 oz) fresh raspberries
200 g (7 oz) low-fat lemon yoghurt
10 ice cubes, crushed
mint leaves, to garnish

1. Put all the ingredients in a blender and process at high speed until smooth.
2. Pour into 2 tall glasses and serve immediately, garnished with mint leaves.

LEMON LOUPY SMOOTHIE

Serves 3–4

200 g (7 oz) lemon low-fat yoghurt
30 ml (2 tbsp) lemon juice
350 g (12 oz) cantaloupe, rind removed, seeded and chopped
115 g (4 oz) lemon sorbet

1. Combine the lemon yoghurt, lemon juice and cantaloupe in a blender and blend on high speed until the cantaloupe is puréed and the mixture is smooth.
2. Add the lemon sorbet, blend again until smooth and serve immediately.

INDIAN MANGO SMOOTHIE

Serves 4

   2 ripe mangoes, peeled, stoned and diced
   225 g (8 oz) low-fat plain yoghurt
   180 ml (6 fl oz) low-fat milk
   8 ice cubes, crushed
   115 g (4 oz) caster sugar
   5 g (1 tsp) ground cardamom

Put all the ingredients into a blender and process until smooth.

MANGO AND PINEAPPLE SMOOTHIE

Makes 3–4 servings

   225 g (8 oz) vanilla or peach low-fat yoghurt
   120 ml (4 fl oz) orange juice
   1 medium mango, stoned and chopped
   280 g (10 oz) fresh pineapple cubes
   115 g (4 oz) frozen banana slices

1. Combine the yoghurt, orange juice, mango and pineapple in a blender. Blend on high speed until mango is puréed and mixture is smooth.
2. Add banana slices and blend on high speed until smooth. Serve immediately.

MORNING GLORY

Serves 3–4

> 240 ml (8 fl oz) orange juice
>
> 3 clementines or satsumas, peeled, pith removed and chopped
>
> 1 grapefruit, any colour, peeled, pith and seeds removed and chopped
>
> 15 ml (1 tbsp) lime juice
>
> 225 g (8 oz) orange sorbet

1. Combine orange juice, clementines or satsumas, grapefruit and lime juice in a blender and blend on high until the fruit is puréed and the mixture is smooth.

2. Add the sorbet and blend again until smooth. Serve immediately.

ORANGE ROYALE SMOOTHIE

This very orange-coloured smoothie is just bursting with betacarotene.

Serves 4

> 2 fresh ripe apricots, stoned
>
> 1/2 mango, peeled and sliced
>
> 1 papaya, peeled and chopped
>
> 1/4 cantaloupe, peeled and chopped
>
> 2 oranges, juiced
>
> 360 ml (12 fl oz) fresh carrot juice

1. Put all the ingredients into a blender and process on medium speed for 1 minute.

2. Pour into a jug and chill in the refrigerator until cold.

3. Whisk to combine, pour into glasses and serve.

ORANGE-PINEAPPLE PASSION

Serves 3–4
>   175 g (6 oz) silken tofu
>   120 ml (4 fl oz) orange juice
>   450 g (1 lb) fresh pineapple, chopped
>   176 g (6 oz) passion fruit sorbet

1. Combine tofu, orange juice and pineapple in a blender. Blend on high speed until the pineapple is puréed and the mixture is smooth.
2. Add the sorbet and blend again until the mixture is smooth. Serve immediately.

PEACHY KEEN SMOOTHIE

Serves 3–4
180 ml (6 fl oz) orange juice
225 g (8 oz) low-fat peach yoghurt
2 large peaches, peeled, stoned, sliced and frozen
115 g (4 oz) vanilla or peach frozen yoghurt or ice cream
Dash of almond essence (optional)

1. Combine orange juice, yoghurt and peaches in a blender. Blend on high speed until peaches are puréed and mixture is smooth.
2. Add frozen yoghurt or ice cream and almond essence, if using. Blend on high speed again until smooth. Serve immediately.

PINK PANTHER SMOOTHIE

This sweet fruit recipe is great for breakfast, an afternoon snack, or for dessert.

Serves 2

225 g (8 oz) fresh strawberries
115 g (4 oz) chopped watermelon
Juice of 2 freshly squeezed oranges
Juice of 1 freshly squeezed lime
120 ml (4 fl oz) ruby red grapefruit juice

Put all the ingredients into a blender and process until smooth. Cover and chill. Before serving, shake or stir, then pour into chilled glasses.

POMEGRANATE PARADISE

This is paradise indeed and full of wonderful fruit.

Serves 2

240 ml (8 fl oz) pomegranate juice
140 g (5 oz) fresh or frozen strawberries
1 small mango, peeled and stoned
1 fresh peach, stoned and chunked

Put all the ingredients into a blender and whizz until smooth. One sip and you'll think you're in paradise!

RED, WHITE AND BLUEBERRY SMOOTHIE

Serves 2

1 large banana, cut into pieces and frozen
4 large fresh strawberries
85 g (3 oz) fresh or frozen blueberries

240 ml (8 fl oz) low-fat milk
5 ml (1 tsp) vanilla essence
60 ml (4 tbsp) vanilla low-fat yoghurt
5 ice cubes, crushed

Put all the ingredients into a blender and process until smooth.

STRAWBERRY COCO LOCO SMOOTHIE

Serves 4
180 ml (6 fl oz) low-fat milk
200 ml (7 fl oz) coconut cream
450 g (1 lb) frozen unsweetened strawberries
4 fresh strawberries, to garnish

Put all the ingredients except the fresh strawberries into a blender and process until smooth, stopping to scrape down the sides. Pour into 4 glasses and garnish with fresh strawberries.

STRAWBERRY KIWI SMOOTHIE

Serves 2–3

200 ml (7 fl oz) vanilla or strawberry low-fat yoghurt
4 medium kiwi fruit, peeled
120 ml (4 fl oz) orange juice
115 g (4 oz) caster sugar
225 g (8 oz) frozen strawberries

Put all the ingredients except the strawberries into a blender and process until smooth. Add the strawberries and process again until smooth.

'HOT' TOMATO SMOOTHIE

Tomatoes are full of lovely lycopene, which will help prevent prostate cancer.

Serves 4

2 large tomatoes, chopped
120 ml (4 fl oz) fresh tomato juice
1 small carrot, chopped
60 ml (4 tbsp) chopped celery
Tabasco sauce, to taste
10 ice cubes

Put all the ingredients into a blender and process until smooth.

TROPICAL FIVE-FRUIT SMOOTHIE

Serves 2

1 large banana, peeled and cut into chunks
2 kiwi fruit, peeled
1/2 mango, peeled and sliced

¼ papaya, peeled and sliced
240 ml (8 fl oz) fresh orange juice
4 ice cubes, crushed

Put all the ingredients into a blender and process until smooth.

VANILLA-DATE SMOOTHIE

Serves 2
200 g (7 oz) vanilla low-fat yoghurt
240 ml (8 fl oz) low-fat milk or vanilla soya milk
250 g (9 oz) stoned Medjool dates
10 ice cubes

Put the yoghurt, milk and dates into a blender and process until smooth. Add the ice cubes and process again until the mixture is thick and smooth.

WAKE-UP WONDER DRINK

This drink provides calcium from the yoghurt and vitamin C from the strawberries.

Serves 4
480 ml (16 fl oz) milk or soya milk
115 g (4 oz) plain bio yoghurt
250 g (9 oz) strawberries, washed and hulled
4 passion fruits, halved and flesh scooped out
20 ml (4 tsp) shelled hemp seeds
20 ml (4 tsp) honey

Put all the ingredients into a blender and process until smooth.

WATERMELON SMOOTHIE

Serves 4

450 g (1 lb) watermelon cubes

175 g (6 oz) cantaloupe cubes

60 g (2 oz) strawberries

200 g (7 oz) vanilla low-fat yoghurt

10 ice cubes

Put all the ingredients into a blender and process until smooth.

BEAUTY SMOOTHIES

BEAUTY SMOOTHIES

The same nutrients that make fruit so good for your body — you are what you eat, after all — are also a great boon for the skin.

Here are a few recipes that will calm, correct, nourish and replenish. Your skin never had it so good and it's all natural and inexpensive to make.

Remember, it's always a good idea to do a patch test before using any home-made beauty recipe.

THE CELLULITE SOLUTION SMOOTHIE

Serves 1

 120 ml (4 fl oz) unsweetened pomegranate juice
 120 ml (4 fl oz) soya milk
 55 g (2 oz) fresh or frozen blueberries
 15 ml (1 tbsp) lecithin powder
 15 ml (1 tbsp) ground flaxseed
 30 ml (2 tbsp) dried goji berries
 4 ice cubes, crushed
 Granulated sugar substitute (optional)

Put all the ingredients into a blender and process until smooth.

FANTASTIC SKIN BODY MASK

Although fruit in any form is a delight to eat, your skin can also benefit from a fruit salad smoothie. Pineapple sloughs off dead skin cells, grapes protect against harmful ultraviolet rays, and other fruits hydrate and soothe sunburnt or troubled skin.

2 slices fresh pineapple, peeled

$1/2$ honeydew melon, rind removed

12 green seedless grapes

1 banana, peeled and cut into chunks

1 kiwi fruit, peeled

1. Put all the ingredients into a blender and process. The mixture will be slightly lumpy.
2. Chill in the refrigerator for 1 hour.
3. Smooth onto the body and leave on for 30 minutes.
4. Rinse off with warm water.

SENSATIONAL STRAWBERRY SKINCARE SMOOTHIES

Strawberries are not only delicious to eat, they are also very beneficial to the skin. Here are some ideas for strawberry smoothies for the skin.

KIWI CUCUMBER STRAWBERRY FACIAL CLEANSER

Blend 5 to 6 strawberries, 1 kiwi, peeled, and $1/2$ cucumber to a smooth paste. If the mixture is slightly runny, add a bit of porridge oats until the potion is of proper consistency. Apply to your face and neck area with gentle massage to exfoliate the skin. Let the paste settle on your skin for 10 minutes and then rinse well with warm water. Your skin will feel fresh and clean.

STRAWBERRY FACE MASK

Combine 2 or 3 ripe strawberries with 30 ml (2 tbsp) of finely ground porridge oats and 1 drop of lemon essential oil to form a paste. Spread the paste on to the face and neck area with the fingertips. Relax for 20 minutes. Rinse off with cool water followed by a toner and moisturiser. The strawberry seeds aid in the skin treatment process.

ANTIOXIDANT MASK WITH STRAWBERRY AND PAPAYA

½ papaya
4 strawberries
15 ml (1 tbsp) porridge oats
5 ml (1 tsp) honey
5 ml (1 tsp) fresh lemon juice

Process the papaya, strawberries and oats in a blender until smooth and add warm honey until it is flowing freely. Mix well. Apply this mixture to the face and let it remain for 15 minutes. Rinse with warm water followed with moisturiser.

FACE-LIFTING MASK

3 to 4 strawberries
5 to 6 grapes
½ pear
½ apple
30 ml (2 tbsp) orange juice
Honey and vinegar to finish

Put all the strawberries, grapes, pear, apple and orange juice into a blender and process until smooth.

Before applying this paste, coat your face with honey. Cover with the fruit mixture. Leave on for 30 minutes and then rinse with lukewarm water. For the final rinse, use vinegar to give your face a perfect lift.